Mechanized Warfare in Color

TANKS
and other A.F.V.s of the
Blitzkrieg Era
1939 to 1941

by
B. T. WHITE

illustrated by
JOHN WOOD

The Macmillan Company
New York, New York

Library of Congress Catalog Card Number: 72–78616

First American edition 1972
First published in Great Britain in 1972 by
Blandford Press Ltd, London

THE MACMILLAN COMPANY
866 Third Avenue, New York, N.Y. 10022

Printed in Great Britain

PREFACE

This book covers the period 1939–41. In order to be able to compare tanks and other armoured fighting vehicles which were actually in service during this time, vehicles whose development began some years earlier have in some cases been included. The period of development for a new A.F.V. had increased from as little as a few months during the First World War to several years in many instances in the peacetime 1930s. However, in the majority of cases, the older A.F.V.s in this book were still in production (in their latest models, at any rate) in 1939.

Strict chronology has not been possible because exact dates of design, commencement of production, entry into service, etc., have not always been ascertainable. Also, to complicate matters, there were of course differing dates for successive models of a particular type. A broad chronology has been followed, however, though to add interest a certain amount of grouping has been used to bring associated A.F.V.s together.

Vehicles are shown as far as possible in accurate colours for the period, where the information has been obtainable. More detailed notes on this subject are contained in an appendix at the end of the book.

To supplement the coloured illustrations and text, cross-sectional drawings of a small number of A.F.V.s have been included in order to show typical internal layouts. These are not to scale but the overall length of each vehicle is given.

Many sources of information have been used in the preparation of this book and grateful thanks are due to many of the author's friends—but among them particular reference must be made to Colonel Robert J. Icks and to Colonel Peter Hordern, Director of the Royal Armoured Corps Tank Museum, Bovington, Dorset.

Mention must also be made of the two excellent A.F.V. modellers' journals (details of which appear in the Appendix on A.F.V. camouflage) and the helpful reference departments of the Imperial War Museum, London. Last, but not least, without the co-operation of my wife, both in typing the manuscript and in keeping my two sons out of the way, this book could never have been completed.

B. T. WHITE
London 1972

INTRODUCTION

Blitzkrieg, 1939–41

Blitzkrieg ('lightning war') was the term which came to mean, in 1939–40, the successes of German arms, led by tanks, beginning with the invasion of Poland in September 1939 and followed, in April–June 1940, by the conquest of Denmark, Norway, Holland, Belgium, Luxembourg and France.

Britain narrowly escaped defeat in 1940 only because the major part of the British Expeditionary Force was evacuated from Dunkirk, but without its tanks and heavy equipment.

Before this, in northern Europe, Russia, which had joined in the attack on Poland in 1939, had moved against Finland at the end of November. Although the end was not in doubt, the Finns succeeded in capturing much Russian equipment, including tanks, before surrendering in March 1940.

Italy entered the war on Germany's side in June 1940 and the defeat of the Italian Army in Libya between November 1940 and the early part of 1941 was the first of a string of Allied victories. This was, however, only the beginning of a long series of North African battles, in which the German Afrika Korps joined in March 1941.

Then, following the final abandonment of 'Operation Sea Lion', the planned German invasion of England, came the massive attack on Russia in June 1941. Some of the greatest tank battles of all were to take place on Soviet territory before the war ended.

The two other great powers, the U.S.A. and Japan, came into the world conflict at the very end of 1941.

However, apart from token U.S. equipment covered in this volume, the armour of these countries is better dealt with later in the series.

Technical Development

The wide range of A.F.V. designs from all the countries involved in a world war cannot satisfactorily be summarised in a short introduction like this, and only broad trends can be mentioned, more detail being left to the descriptions and illustrations of A.F.V.s in the main part of the book.

The widest single influence in A.F.V. design in 1939 was probably still that of the British firm of Vickers-Armstrongs Ltd. Light tanks ranging from 2 to 7 tons supplied by Vickers-Armstrongs, built under licence, or inspired by Vickers-Armstrongs' designs, formed a high proportion of the armoured forces of the U.S.S.R. (T-26 series), Poland (TK series and 7 TP), Germany (PzKpfw IA and B, derived from Vickers-Carden-Loyd designs), Italy and France (L.3/35 and Renault UE, both based on a Carden-Loyd design), as well as of Britain. These tanks were all of simple and relatively cheap but reliable and effective design. Most were lightly armoured but some, such as the Russian T-26s, were very well armed for their size. The British Cruiser tanks Marks I and II and the Valentine (the British tank built in the greatest numbers in the Second World War) were also Vickers-Armstrongs' designs.

The American Christie designs were another, and more enduring, influence on A.F.V. development, and Russia,

Poland and Britain used J. Walter Christie's principles of a good cross-country suspension system with a high-powered engine for fast medium tanks. The Russian BT series (the most numerous Soviet tank in 1939) and the British Cruiser Mark III were successfully developed into the T-34 and later cruiser tanks respectively, used to the end of the war and after.

Other medium tanks ranged from the German PzKpfw III, intended as the basic tank of the Panzer divisions, which was armed with a 3·7-cm. gun and was fairly mobile but armoured only to a maximum of 30 mm., to the French Somua S.35. This tank had cast armour up to 55 mm., a 47-mm. gun and a quite good performance, and was considered one of the best of its class in the world in 1939, although, unlike the German tank, it probably lacked the potential for much further development. French tanks, whose development was to cease after June 1940, had relatively poor suspension systems but in many cases had advanced transmissions and steering and, except for the light cavalry reconnaissance vehicles, were well armoured, much use being made of large castings for hulls and turrets. Welding techniques were also successfully applied to armour in, for example, the F.C.M.36. Good examples of well-balanced designs of light-medium tanks were the Czech LT-35 and LT-38, both of which were sold commercially before 1939. Supplies of these tanks, and their production lines, were invaluable to Germany's later plans when Czechoslovakia was annexed in March 1939. Britain's Infantry Tank, Mark II, although often limited in use by the official infantry supporting concept to which it was designed, was in 1939-40 one of the best tanks in the world in the medium category. Although compact, it was very well armoured, well armed and reasonably mobile.

Self-propelled artillery was mainly a German speciality in 1939-40, with both improvised mountings on PzKpfw I chassis and specialised 'assault guns', although the French Char B and the Russian KV II were different approaches to the problem of bringing artillery into action close to the centre of the battle.

Armoured car design of the older school was characterised by the Polish wz 34 which used a conventional 4 × 2 chassis, and by the Russian BA-10 which, because of its six-wheeled chassis, had a rather better cross-country performance. The German SdKfz 231(6-rad) series was also in this category, but exhibited a much more advanced design of ballistically thought-out armoured hull. Ahead in their mechanical concepts were the rear-engined Dutch DAF six-wheeler (which was well armed and had a good hull design), the French Panhard 178, which first came into service in 1935, and the Swedish Pb. m/39-40. Britain's modern armoured car was the Guy Tank, Light (Wheeled) Mark I which was similar in layout to the Panhard and also had 4 × 4 drive with 'solid' axles. The large German eight-wheeled armoured cars, the small British Scout Car, Mark I and the Italian AB.40 all showed more advanced mechanical features for suspension and all-wheel-drive transmission.

Armoured personnel carriers for the transport of infantry accompanying the

2

tanks were employed significantly only by the Germans in 1939–40, the vehicle type being the half-tracked SdKfz 251 and, later, the SdKfz 250 series. These vehicles were rather complicated in design but highly efficient, and were also used for many other purposes. The French were the only other country to employ half-tracks in action at this time, although the armoured ones were represented principally by the Schneider P.16 used as an Automitrailleuse de Combat alongside full-tracked light tanks. The only Allied armoured personnel carrier during this period was the wheeled American White Scout Car (so called) supplied to Britain in 1941. However, the British full-tracked carriers performed some of the same functions as the German half-tracks. The Russians simply carried infantry on the backs of tanks.

Armoured Command Vehicles were represented by modified German tanks on PzKpfw I and III chassis, together with wireless versions of the armoured half-tracks and armoured cars. All British tanks were wireless-equipped (unlike some German and Russian tanks at the early stages of the war) so command was relatively easy, but British A.C.V.s like the Guy Lizard did not appear until late 1940 and, at a lower command level, the White Scout Car was used for this purpose from 1941 onwards.

Designs for special forms of tanks or other assault vehicles were called for to meet particular problems. The breaching of the Siegfried Line could, it was hoped in 1939–40, be carried out by the British A.22 (later known as Infantry Mark IV), or by T.O.G. heavy assault tanks, or by the N.L.E. Trenching Machine. A French approach was a design for a special version of the Somua-Coder bridging device, although this was never built. The German 'Operation Sea Lion' required the use of amphibious tanks and a Schwimmpanzer II was built, together with submersible versions of PzKpfw III and IV. The United Kingdom was never invaded, but the submersible tanks were used in crossing the River Bug at the opening of the invasion of Russia in June 1941. To counter the expected German landings, Britain produced in a matter of months large numbers of improvised armoured cars to help fill the gap left by the loss of the British Expeditionary Force's tanks. All used standard lorry or passenger car chassis and some of the more important are shown in this book. Others were 'armoured' with concrete or with boxes filled with pebbles.

The Irish Free State also built in 1940–41 armoured cars (similar in layout to the Polish wz 34 and many others of this type) to defend their neutrality, and another neutral, Sweden, continued the development of the Landsverk series of armoured cars and tanks. Swedish armoured fighting vehicles were, at this time, well up to the standard of their contemporaries in the bigger countries, the tanks having torsion-bar suspension and geared steering.

Power plants were diverse in British and French tanks in 1939–40, varying from slightly modified commercial engines to specially designed tank engines. Some were diesels, but these were in the minority. Germany had concentrated solely on petrol engines for all her tanks and had standardised on a range built by Maybach, with advantages in the supply of components and spares. The Italians, on the other hand, chose a diesel for their medium tanks and this was one of their best features. The Russians had a fairly wide range of engines in use in 1949 but they concentrated their efforts on the development of a good twelve-cylinder diesel engine of around 500 h.p. This powerful engine was successfully used in the KV and T-34 tanks and lasted throughout the war.

Suspension systems varied widely in most countries over this period, only the Italians continuing to favour the leaf springs controlling groups of road wheels which were common in the pre-war Vickers designs. The French tended to prefer coil-spring systems of various sorts (sometimes using rubber washers in compression instead) and Britain (after the Cruisers Marks I and II and Infantry Marks I–III) generally used independent coil-spring suspensions of one type or another, the Christie system being standardised for Cruiser tanks. After many experiments with all the early versions of their principal tanks in use by 1939, the Germans settled on transverse torsion bars for the PzKpfw III and quarter-elliptic leaf springs, in different layouts, for the PzKpfw IV and standard models of PzKpfw II. The Russians had various suspension systems on their older tanks in use in 1939 but retained the Christie system of the BT in developing the T-34 (omitting the ability to run on wheels) and used torsion bars for the KV series and also for new light tanks.

Steering systems generally tended to advance from the crude clutch and brake (skid-turn) type to geared arrangements of varying degrees of sophistication. The British Bren Carrier's track-bowing system for gentle turns, before bringing in the clutch and brake, is worthy of mention here because it was one of the few of its kind.

Armament and armour have been left to last because, given that a tank has some degree of mobility, they are the most important features.

Armour increased steadily in thickness between 1939 and 1941 but although some effective designs, such as the DAF armoured car, had shown the way, little real attempt to improve its arrangement on tanks for maximum effect seems to have been made before the appearance of the Russian T-34. An example of these increases is the British Cruiser Mark I, which had a 14-mm. armour maximum, whereas the Cruiser Mark V (Covenanter) had nearly trebled this to 40 mm. before the end of 1940. An exceptionally well-armoured tank in 1939, with a 60-mm. maximum, was the British Infantry Mark I, but for the Infantry Mark IV, prototypes of which appeared before the end of 1940, 102 mm. was considered necessary. British armour protection was to some extent accelerated because of the delay in production of a heavier offensive weapon than the 2-pounder, but on the German PzKpfw III, the original 14·5-mm. maximum went up to 30 mm. on Ausf.E and climbed to 50 mm. on some models before the end of 1941. Armament also showed a steady increase between 1939 and 1941 in calibre and/or penetrative ability. Even for light tanks after 1940 the heavy machine-guns or rifles that served as anti-tank guns generally could no longer be regarded as worth while, although they continued in use for armoured cars. Perhaps the most dramatic contrast was of the 45-mm. gun, generally used as an armour-piercing weapon in many older Russian tanks in 1939, with the powerful 76·2-mm. gun (L/30·5 calibre, soon to be increased to L/41·2) of the KV I and T-34. This gun was capable of firing solid armour-piercing shot and high-explosive ammunition, a feature absent in the British 2-pounder (40-mm.) gun which was in its time an excellent armour-piercing weapon.

The German encounter in 1941 with these two powerful Russian tanks, and particularly the T-34, marked a watershed in A.F.V. design because they were so much better in all essentials than tanks of other countries on both sides.

Armoured Formations

The successes of the German Panzer forces in 1939–41 are attributable to a high degree of training and organisation and not just to numbers of tanks or their quality.

In Poland, where only some 700 tanks (the majority tankettes of the TK type), mostly dispersed among various unarmoured formations, were mobilised and available to oppose about 2,000 German tanks (many of which were, admittedly, also light) organised into seven Panzer Divisions and four light divisions, the final outcome was predictable.

The Panzer forces for the campaign in the West in May 1940 had no such overall superiority, however. The French had a quite considerable armoured force of about 3,000 modern tanks, of which some 800 were medium or heavy tanks. There were two types of armoured formation, the Divisions Légères Méchaniques (D.L.M.) of which three existed in May 1940, and the Division Cuirassée (D.C.R.) of which there were also three, with a fourth still in the process of formation when the campaign began.

These two types of formation were specified for strategic reconnaissance on the one hand—and the D.L.M. was a mobile and fairly well-balanced formation, although with a preponderance of light tanks and armoured cars—and for the set-piece breakthrough on the other. The D.C.R. was well provided with powerful tanks but lacked both mobility and adequate supporting arms. Some 1,500 tanks of all sizes were contained in formations of this type and the balance of the modern French tanks was distributed in groups of tank battalions attached to the various French Armies along the frontier and behind the Maginot Line defences.

The British Expeditionary Force in France had only one Army Tank Brigade of two battalions of infantry tanks, one armoured division (of which only one of the two armoured brigades arrived in time for the main battle), and numbers of light tanks included in the divisional mechanised cavalry regiments in each infantry division.

Against this Allied force the Germans used some 2,500 tanks, nearly all included in ten panzer divisions, nine of which were concentrated on a narrow front. The French armoured formations were committed piecemeal and apart from slight temporary set-backs such as the attacks of the 1st Army Tank Brigade and de Gaulle's 4e D.C.R., the panzer divisions had it all their own way and the campaign was virtually over in a fortnight.

The same well-tried German tactics were used again in Russia in June 1941, this time with about 3,000 tanks, some 2,000 being PzKpfw IIIs and IVs. To oppose them, the Russians probably had at least 20,000 tanks of all types, although only a relatively small proportion were organised in formations actually at the front. In five months the Germans destroyed or captured around 17,000 Russian tanks against their own losses of 2,700. Almost at the gates of Moscow and almost, it seemed, within sight of final victory, the offensive was halted by the combination of supply problems in the vast country, stubborn Russian resistance and finally, the Russian winter.

THE COLOURED ILLUSTRATIONS

A description of each coloured
plate is given between pages
89 and 146

NOTE

The side views of the Finnish Vickers 6-ton tank (No. 22) and the Polish light tank 7TP (No. 17) have been constructed by the artist. In both cases, the proportions of the suspension should, in fact, correspond closely with that shown in the side view of the Russian T-26B (No. 36).

By a Publisher's error, the Russian T-26B (No. 36) and the Finnish Vickers 6-ton (No. 22) tanks were transposed out of the sequence intended by the author.

Poland

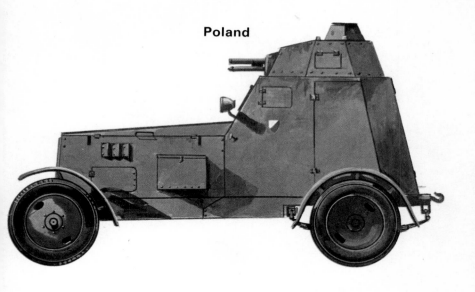

1 Armoured Car wz 34

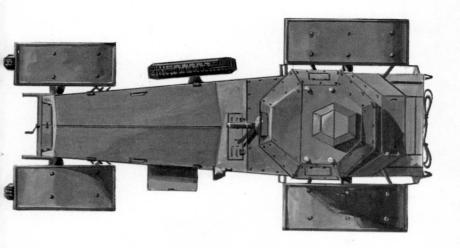

Poland

2 Tankettes TK3 (with 20-mm. gun) (*below*) and TKS

3 Char Moyen Renault D.2

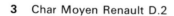

France

4   Chars de Bataille Renault B.1 (*below*) and B.1 bis

5 Char Léger Renault R.35

6 Chars Légers Hotchkiss H.35 (*below*) and H.39

7   Char de Cavalerie Somua S.35

France

8   A.M.C. 1935, Renault type ACG 1

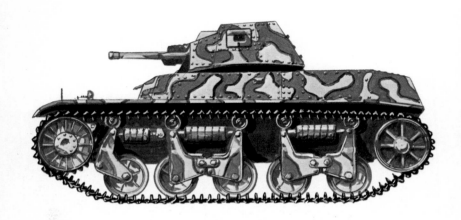

9 A.M.R. 1935, Renault type ZT

France

10   A.M.D. Panhard type 178

11 Chenillette d'infanterie Renault type UE

Italy

12   Carro Armato L.3/35

13   Lehký Tank LT-35 (*above*) and Panzerkampfwagen 35(t)

Belgium

14 Char Léger, Vickers-Carden-Loyd, Modèle T.15

15 Panzerkampfwagen I, Ausf. B

France

16 Char Léger F.C.M. 36

17 Light Tank 7TP

Poland

18   Medium Tank 10TP

19 Schwerer Panzerspähwagen (6-rad) SdKfz 231 (*above*)
and Schwerer Panzerspähwagen (6-rad) (Fu) SdKfz 232

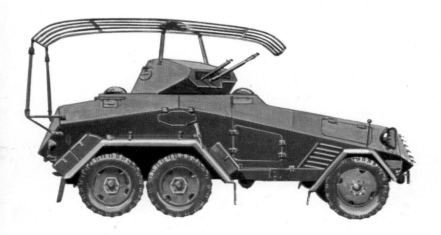

Germany

20 Panzerkampfwagen II, Ausf. c

21 BA-32-2 (Armoured Car)

Finland

22 Tank, Vickers 6-ton (T-26E), with 37-mm. Puteaux gun (*above*) and with 37-mm. Bofors gun

23 BT-7 ('Fast Tank'): BT-7-1 (*below*) and BT-7-2

U.S.S.R.

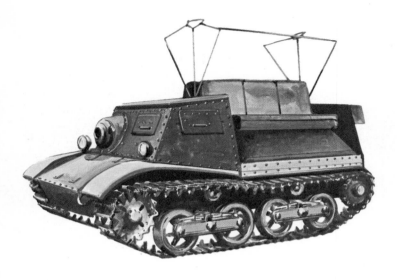

24 STZ Komsomolets (Armoured Tractor)

U.K.

25 Carrier, Bren

26 Carrier, Cavalry, Mark I (*below*) and Carrier, Scout, Mark I

27 Armoured Car, Reconnaissance, Morris (Model CS9/LAC)

Germany

28 Schwerer Panzerspähwagen (8-rad) Sdkfz 231 (chassis) (*below*) and Schwerer Panzerspähwagen (8-rad) (Fu) Sdkfz 232

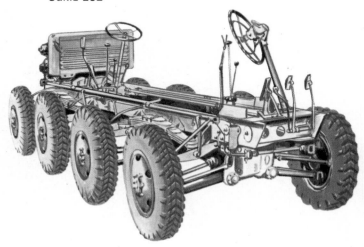

29 Schwere geländegängige gepanzerte Personenkraft-
wagen, SdKfz 247 (6×4) (*above*) and SdKfz 247 (4×4)

Czechoslovakia

30   Panzerkampfwagen 38(t) (LT-38)

31 Porte-Pont, Somua-Coder MSCL-5

32 T-28C (Medium Tank)

33 T-35 (Heavy Tank)

Sweden

34 Pansarbil m/39-40

Sweden

35 Stridsvagn m/39

U.S.S.R.

36 T-26B (Light Tank)

37 Tank, Light, M2A4

38 Scout Car, M3A1

39   Tanks, Light, Mark VIB (*above*) and Mark VIC

40   Tank, Infantry, Mark I

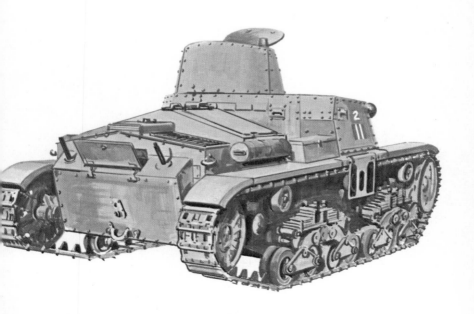

41 Carro Armato M.11/39

Germany

42 Mittlerer Schützenpanzerwagen SdKfz 251/1 (*above*) and Mittlerer Schützenpanzerwagen (Funkwagen) SdKfz 251/3

43 Kleiner Panzerbefehlswagen I

Germany

44   Panzerkampfwagen III, Ausf. E (*below*) and G

45 Panzerkampfwagen IV, Ausf. A (*below*) and B

Germany

46 15-cm. s.I.G. on Panzerkampfwagen I, Ausf. B

47 Panzerjäger I

Holland

48   Pantserwagen M'39 (DAF)

49 Tanks, Cruiser, Mark I (*above*) and Mark ICS

50   Tank, Cruiser, Mark IIA

51 Tanks, Cruiser, Marks IV (*below*) and IVA

52 Tank, Infantry, Mark II, Matilda I

53 Tanks, Light (Wheeled) Marks I (*below*) and IA

U.K.

54   Car, Scout, Mark I

55   KV I(B) (Heavy Tank)

U.S.S.R.

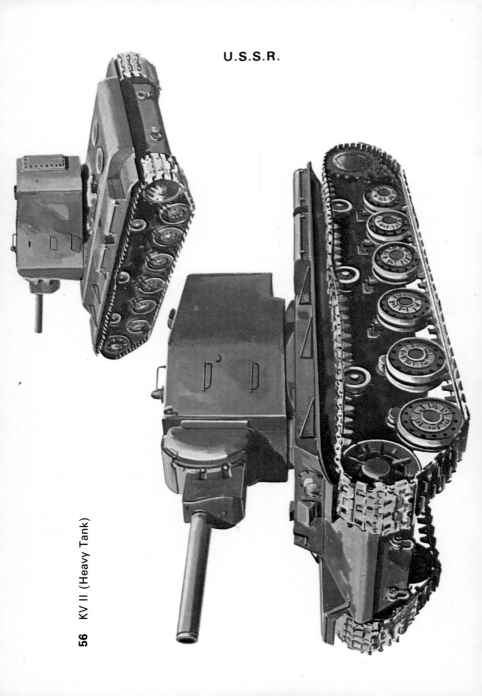

56 KV II (Heavy Tank)

57 South African Reconnaissance Car, Mark II

Germany

58   Leichter Panzerspähwagen SdKfz 222

59 Leichter Schützenpanzerwagen SdKfz 250/1 (*above*) and leichter gepanzerter Munitionstransport Kraftwagen SdKfz 252

Germany

60 Sturmgeschütz III

61 T-34 ('T-34/76A') (Medium Tank)

Italy

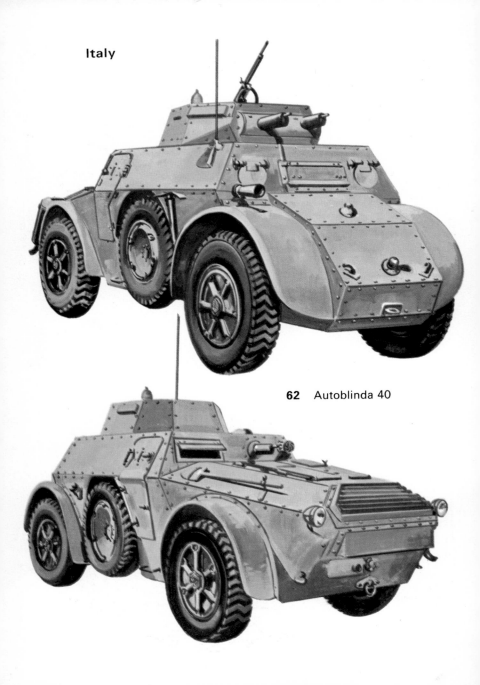

62 Autoblinda 40

Italy

63 Carro Armato L.6/40

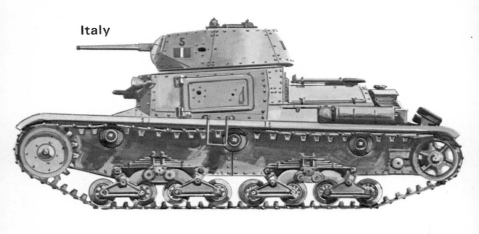

Italy

64   Carro Armato M.13/40

65 Tank, Infantry, Mark III*, Valentine II

66 Cars, 4×2, Light Reconnaissance, Standard, Marks I (*above*) and II (Beaverette I and II)

67 Car, 4×2, Light Reconnaissance, Humber Mark I (Ironside I) (*above*) and Car, 4-seater, Armoured Saloon, Humber (Special Ironside)

68 Armoured Car, Dodge (*above*) and Lorry, 30-cwt, 4 × 2, Armoured Anti-tank, Bedford

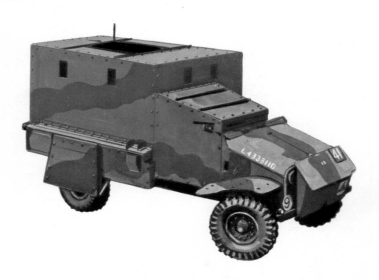

Germany

69 Panzerkampfwagen II (Schwimm.)

70   Panzerkampfwagen II (Flamm.)

71 Tank, Heavy, T.O.G. I

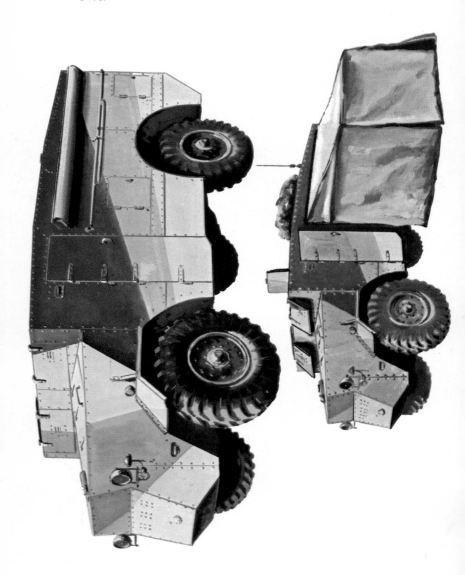

72 Armoured Command Vehicle, Guy 'Lizard'

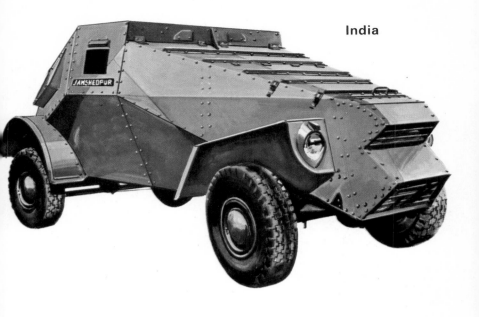

73   Armoured Carrier, Wheeled, I.P. Mark I

U.K.

74 Tank, Cruiser, Mark V, Covenanter I

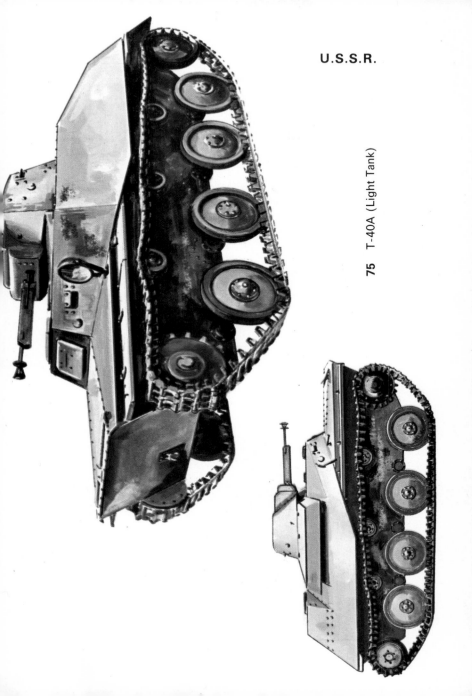

Irish Free State

76 Armoured Car Mark IV (Ford)

77 Cockatrice (Bedford) (*below*) and Heavy Cockatrice (A.E.C.) Flamethrowers

78 Tanks, Infantry, Mark IV, Churchill I (*above*) and Mark IVA, Churchill II

U.K.

79 N.L.E. Trenching Machine, Mark I

U.S.A.

80 Tank Light, M3 (Stuart I)

TANKS AND OTHER ARMOURED
FIGHTING VEHICLES OF THE BLITZKRIEG ERA

1 Armoured Car wz 34, Poland.

Eighty-six of these light armoured cars were built in Poland in 1934, using commercial chassis and the turrets and some of the armour from half-tracked armoured cars that had been constructed in Poland in 1928 on Citroen-Kegresse chassis purchased in France. The layout was conventional for armoured cars of the period, although with only a two-man crew the wz 34 was more compact than some (if rather tall in relation to its length), and the car had a good ground clearance. The suspension consisted of quarter-elliptic leaf springs at the front and semi-elliptics at the rear, where there were dual wheels. The engine was originally a six-cylinder 20-h.p. Citroen with three-speed gearbox, although in later versions (wz 34—I and wz 34—II) 23-h.p. and 25-h.p. Polish Fiat engines with four-speed gearboxes were used instead.

The armament consisted of either one short 37-mm. gun or one 7·92-mm. machine-gun in the turret. The armour protection was only 6-mm., though this kept the weight down to under 2½ tons.

The wz 34 armoured cars, together with a smaller number of the older wz 29 pattern, were employed in reconnaissance squadrons in each of the eleven Polish horsed cavalry brigades during the invasion of Poland. The armoured cars were too weak and too few in numbers, however, and were no more able to stand up against the well-equipped German Panzer divisions than were the mounted cavalry.

2 Tankettes TK 3 and TK S, Poland.

A total of nearly 700 of these two-man light tanks or 'tankettes' was built in Poland during the 1930s and at the time of the German invasion the type was by far the strongest in numbers in the Polish armoured forces.

The basic models of the TK 3 and TK S were very much alike in external appearance and both were closely derived from the British Carden-Loyd Mark VI under the licence of which they were built. The chief difference between the two was that the later model, the TK S, had a four-cylinder Polish-built Fiat engine in place of the four-cylinder Ford Model A engine which was used in the TK 3 and the Carden-Loyd. Both the Polish tanks had an enclosed roof of a different design to that of the later enclosed Carden-Loyds and the armour was up to a maximum of 8 mm. in the TK 3 and 10 mm. in the TK S. The standard armament was, in both cases, a 7·92-mm. machine-gun mounted in the front right-hand side of the hull.

Various experimental models of the TK 3 and TK S were produced with improvements in the armament, and the best of these was a version of the TK 3 in which a 20-mm. cannon, mounted in a slightly extended gunner's compartment, replaced the machine-gun. It was planned to have at least a proportion of the tanks in each company of TK 3s or TK Ss rearmed with 20-mm. guns, but only relatively few tanks of this version were in service by September 1939. At this date each of eighteen infantry divisions and eleven (horsed) cavalry brigades had a company of TK 3 or TK S tanks, and the two motorised cavalry brigades included two companies each. Although numerically fairly impressive, this equipment was completely outclassed by the German tanks which it encountered when Poland was invaded.

3 Char Moyen Renault D.2, France.

Direct in line of descent from the light Renault FT of 1917 through the NC 27 and NC 31 (sold abroad but not used by France), the Char D.2 was one of the first modern types of infantry medium tanks to be supplied to the French Army after the First World War.

The Renault-designed D.2 had a rear-mounted engine—a six-cylinder Renault of 150 h.p.—with transmission via a four-speed gearbox to rear sprockets. The crew compartment and turret were set fairly well forward, the cast turret mounting a 47-mm. gun and one 7·5-mm. machine-gun. Armour was to a maximum of 40 mm. and the top speed was 15 m.p.h. The suspension, protected by hinged side skirting plates, consisted on each side of three bogie units of four road wheels and sprung on vertical coil springs. Additionally there were single road wheels each side in front of and behind the bogie groups. First appearing in 1933, the Char D.2 was largely superseded by the Char B series by 1940. Nevertheless, the D.2 still remained in first-line service and formed part of the equipment of General de Gaulle's 4e Division Cuirassée.

4 Chars de Bataille Renault B.1 and B.1 bis, France.

Chars B represented the principal striking force of the four French armoured divisions (Divisions Cuirassées—D.C.R.) that were in existence by 15 May 1940 (the last, under the command of General de Gaulle, created on this day) and, as such, were perhaps the most significant Allied tanks of the era. Each of these divisions had an establishment of four battalions of combat tanks, organised by 1940 in a demi-brigade of two battalions of Chars B.1 bis and a demi-brigade of two battalions of much lighter tanks, in most cases H.39s.

The specification for the Char B had its origin as far back as 1921, but this was not agreed in a final form until 1926 and three prototypes were built between 1929 and 1931. From trials of these emerged the first production model, Char B.1, the earliest of which were completed about 1935.

The Char B showed the influence of the First World War traditions in its long, high profile, but its armour was good for its time, and its armament—a short 75-mm. gun, a 47-mm. gun and two machine-guns—was powerful, although the heavy weapon was limited in use by its mounting low in the hull front. Mobility, too, was not neglected because a six-cylinder Renault engine of 250 h.p. gave a top speed of 17 m.p.h. Steering was by means of an advanced regenerative controlled differential system, by means of which also the 75-mm. gun, which had no independent traverse, could be laid.

The second production model, Char B.1 bis (all of which went to the four D.C.R.), had a 47-mm. turret gun model SA 35, with a longer barrel than the model SA 34 of the B.1, and a 300-h.p. engine which increased the overall performance generally and the top speed slightly, although the radius of action was reduced. The maximum armour protection of 40 mm. in B.1 was increased to 60 mm. in the B.1 bis. A third model, B.1 ter (of which only five were built), had a 350-h.p. diesel engine, the incorporation of limited independent traverse for the 75-mm. gun and redesigned side armour.

Production of the Char B series was undertaken by Renault, Schneider, F.C.M., F.A.M.H. (Saint Chamond) and AMX and about 380 were built, all of which were B.1 bis except for thirty-five of the earlier B.1. Some of those that remained intact after the Campaign of 1940 were used by the Germans as training vehicles, flame-throwers or self-propelled mountings.

5 **Char Léger Renault R.35,** France.

Designed and produced by the Renault company to replace its famous predecessor, the FT 17, the R.35 appeared in 1935. A two-man light tank of just under 10 tons, the R.35 was intended to re-equip the tank regiments supporting infantry divisions and, as such, had relatively heavy armour protection (to a maximum of 45 mm.—greater than that of many contemporary medium tanks of other countries), and a short-barrelled low-velocity 37-mm. gun with coaxial 7·5-mm. machine-gun.

This was at the expense of mobility, because a speed of only 12 m.p.h. was attained with the Renault four-cylinder 82-h.p. engine.

The general layout of the R.35 was conventional, although the use of castings for the turret (pioneered in the Renault FT 17) and parts of the hull was uncommon outside France at the time. The rear-mounted engine drove sprockets at the front of the track and the suspension consisted, each side, of five road wheels and a low-mounted idler wheel at the rear. The road wheels were mounted in two articulated bogies, each of two wheels, and a single. The wheel movement was controlled by springs made up of horizontally mounted rubber washers.

Although production of the R.35 was insufficient completely to replace the FT 17 in the infantry tank regiments, this tank equipped twenty-three battalions and was an important element in the French rearmament programme: it was certainly one of the best-known tanks of its era. Some were also employed in the Divisions Cuirassées in lieu of H.39s.

An improved model of the R.35 had the longer-barrelled SA 38 37-mm. gun and a further development, known as R.40, had an entirely new suspension system designed by AMX with armoured skirting plates. This tank had a far better cross-country performance than the R.35 but only two battalions had been equipped with it by 1940.

6 **Chars Légers Hotchkiss H.35 and H.39,** France.

This light tank was produced at the same time as the Renault R.35 and was adopted by the cavalry, just as the

R.35 was used to re-equip the tank units of the infantry.

The Renault and Hotchkiss tanks were rather alike in appearance and had indentical armament of one 37-mm. gun and one 7·5-mm. machine-gun. The H.35, however, had the special characteristic required by the cavalry of a better speed and this was attained to some extent at the expense of armour protection, which was at a maximum of 34 mm. compared with the infantry tank's 45 mm. The Hotchkiss H.35 had a similar suspension system to the Renault's but using coil springs instead of rubber washers and with one extra road wheel each side: the longer-track base contributing to a better performance cross-country at speed.

In the course of production of the H.35 the original Hotchkiss six-cylinder 75-h.p. engine was replaced by one of 120 h.p. and this increased the maximum speed from 17½ m.p.h. to 22½ m.p.h. The rear hull deck over the engine was higher in this model, known as H.39. Finally, the turret in the later H.39s to be produced was equipped with a long 37-mm. gun.

One of the most important types of French tank of its era, over 1,000 Hotchkiss H.35s and H.39s were produced and with the Somua S.35 they formed the backbone of the cavalry Divisions Légères Méchaniques (DLM) as well as subsequently equipping most of the light battalions in each of the Divisions Cuirassées (DCR) formed in 1939–40.

7 Char de Cavalerie Somua S.35, France.

The Somua S.35 was regarded as the best French tank of the early part of the Second World War and, indeed, was considered by some as one of the best medium tanks of its era in the world. Certainly, after the surrender of France in 1940 this was one of the few types of French tank to be used by the Germans to equip some of their own tank units.

Produced by the Societé d'Outillage Méchanique et Usinage d'Artillerie (SOMUA), the S.35 first appeared in 1935. Intended for the mechanised cavalry, it was originally classified as an Automitrailleuse de Combat (AMC) but later was designated Char de Cavalerie and became one of the principal fighting vehicles of the Divisions Légères Méchaniques. Each of these mechanised cavalry divisions had one regiment (two squadrons) of S.35s in its tank brigade, together with a regiment of Hotchkiss H.39s.

The Somua S.35 shared a common turret design with the Char B.1 bis but had few other similarities with the heavier vehicle. The S.35 had a good road speed of 25 m.p.h. without undue sacrifice of armour protection, which was up to 55 mm, and although the hull was somewhat high the armour was rounded and well-shaped to a design facilitated by the cast form of manufacture used.

The armament of one 47-mm. gun and one 7·5-mm. machine-gun in an electrically traversed turret was as good as or better than that of the majority of German tanks in 1940, although the tank's performance in action was retarded by the fact that the commander was also the gunner.

Power was supplied by a Somua V-8 engine of 190 h.p. linked to a synchromesh five-speed gearbox which transmitted the drive to the tracks via rear sprockets. The steering was of the double differential type offering one radius of turn for each of the five forward gears. The suspension consisted of small road wheels in pairs sprung on leaf springs and protected by side armour skirting.

8 A.M.C. 1935, Renault type ACG 1, France.

This light combat cavalry tank ('Automitrailleuse de Combat') was one of the most advanced French tanks for its size in that as well as being equipped with a good gun it had a two-man turret—the first French tank to do so—with all the advantages in command it conferred.

Designed by Renault, the AMC 35 used suspension of similar design to that of the R.35, but the hull and turret were redesigned and used a bolted or riveted form of construction instead of cast. As required of a cavalry tank, a reasonably good maximum speed of 25 m.p.h. was attained, thanks to the satisfactory power/weight ratio conferred by the 180-h.p. Renault six-cylinder engine. The armament consisted of a 7·5-mm. machine-gun and either a 47-mm. gun (as shown in the pictures) or a high-velocity 25-mm. cannon.

Manufacture of the AMC 35 was undertaken by l'Atelier d'Issy les Moulineaux (AMX) and, somewhat surprisingly, for in retrospect this seems to have been one of the best pre-war French light tank designs, only 100 were built. Some tanks of this type were supplied to the Belgian Army.

9 A.M.R. 1935, Renault type ZT, France.

Designed by Renault for the French cavalry, this light tank was a battle reconnaissance vehicle in the category of 'Automitrailleuse de Reconnaissance' (AMR), to follow the earlier Renault model 33, type VM.

Known by its manufacturers as type ZT, the AMR 35 had the main characteristic demanded of this class of tank of high speed (37 m.p.h.), although at the expense of armour protection which was in the 5–13 mm. range. The armament was, however, an improvement over its predecessor in that the second model (shown in the illustrations) had a 13·2-mm. heavy machine-gun (in place of the 7·5-mm. machine-gun of the AMR 33 and first model of AMR 35). In the final model of AMR 35 a 25-mm. gun was fitted.

The mechanical layout of the AMR 35 was similar to that of most French light tanks of the period—a rear-mounted engine (four-cylinder Renault, 80-h.p.) with drive to front sprockets. The suspension consisted, each side, of one pair of road wheels and two singles controlled by rubber washers in compression—a system also used in the R.35 and H.35. The two-man crew occupied the centre part of the vehicle, the driver at the left. The turret was also at the left-hand side of the hull, the engine being at the right.

Nearly 200 of these tanks were built and many were still in service in 1939–40, although it was the intention to replace them with the slower but much better-protected Hotchkiss H.35.

10 **A.M.D. Panhard type 178,** France.

This Automitrailleuse de Découverte, which was designed in 1933, first entered service with the French Army in 1935, and today still looks modern in appearance, was one of the best armoured cars of its kind in the world in the early part of the Second World War.

Known as the Panhard type 178 to its manufacturers and as AMD Panhard modèle 1935 by the French Army, this was the first four-wheeled, four-wheel-drive rear-engined armoured car to go into series production for a major country and the same layout was subsequently adopted by the United Kingdom, Germany, the United States and Italy, among others.

Power was provided by a four-cylinder Panhard-type S.K. engine of 105 h.p. and transmitted through a gearbox with four forward and four reverse speeds. The maximum speed was 45 m.p.h. The crew of four included a second driver at the rear, and a speed of 26 m.p.h. could be attained in reverse.

Early examples of the Panhard 178 had a short-calibre gun or, in some cases, two machine-guns but the standard armament was a 25-mm. high-velocity gun and one 7·5-mm. machine-gun mounted coaxially in the turret. A command version had a fixed structure replacing the turret and was without armament. The armour protection of the Panhard was in the range 20 mm. maximum and 7 mm. minimum.

The Panhard armoured cars were used by the mechanised cavalry for long-distance reconnaissance in the reconnaissance regiments of the Divisions Légères Méchaniques (D.L.M.), and in the so-called reconnaissance groups of infantry divisions (G.R.D.I.): in both types of unit they were grouped with cavalry full-tracked or half-tracked armoured vehicles. After the defeat of France in 1940, the Germans acknowledged the merit of the Panhard 178 by taking all those available into service in the German Army, where they received the designation of Pz. Spähwagen P.204(f).

11 **Chenillette d'infanterie Renault type UE,** France.

This small tracked vehicle was produced in large numbers from 1931 onwards as an armoured supply tractor for the French infantry. Weighing only about 2 tons, its own carrying capacity was slight, but a tracked trailer was normally towed. Both tractor and trailer were derived from Carden-Loyd designs and a very similar vehicle, the Carden-Loyd Mark VI, was widely used by the British Army in the 1930s although, unlike its French contemporary, it had been superseded by the outbreak of the Second World War.

Although a version of the Renault UE with a mounted machine-gun for the co-driver was built, the great majority were unarmed and intended purely as front-line supply vehicles. They were fully enclosed, with light armour protection up to a maximum of 7 mm. The trailer, which could carry about 500 kg., was open and unprotected, and could be used with or without tracks.

The Renault UE was powered by a four-cylinder Renault 35-h.p. engine mounted between the two members of the crew.

12 Carro Armato L.3/35, Italy.

Yet another member of the family of the Carden-Loyd Mark VI, which, by direct sales and the granting of manufacturing licences, spread to many of the countries of the world in the 1930s, was this small Italian tank.

Twenty-five Carden-Loyd Mark VIs were purchased by the Italian Army in 1929 and, based on these, a model known as Carro Veloce ('fast tank') C.V.28 was built by the Fiat motor works in conjunction with the Ansaldo armaments concern. This was followed by further models, C.V.29 and C.V. L.3/33. The Carro Veloce L.3/35 was the final model and included some improvements over the L.3/33, although up-dated examples of the earlier model existed and so the differences between the two are often small.

Although still bearing a superficial resemblance to its Carden-Loyd prototype, the L.3/35 was, in fact, greatly improved mechanically and also in several respects as a fighting vehicle but, even so, by 1939 it was heavily outclassed by the tanks of other powers.

The L.3/35's engine was a four-cylinder Fiat of 43 h.p., mounted transversely at the rear with the radiator—a circular type with centrifugal fan—behind it. The transmission was led forward to the clutch and gearbox (with four forward speeds) in front of the driver, with final drive to front track sprockets. The suspension consisted of two three-wheel bogie units

and a single, unsprung, road wheel (just in front of the rear idler wheel) each side. Each bogie unit was sprung on a quarter-elliptic leaf spring.

The fighting compartment of the L.3/35 was in the centre of the vehicle with the two crew members—driver on the right and gunner on the left—sitting side by side. The armoured superstructure varied in that in the earlier tanks built it was constructed of plates riveted on to angle girders whereas in later vehicles bolts were employed. Maximum armour thickness was 13·5 mm. The standard armament was two 8-mm. Breda model 38 machine-guns with a total traverse of 24 degrees, elevation of 15 degrees and depression of 12 degrees. There was also a flamethrower version in which the flame projector replaced one of the machine-guns.

Large numbers of these Carro Veloce (the maximum speed was in fact only 26 m.p.h.; later the designation Carro Armato was used) were built for the Italian Army and were used in the North African Campaigns and, although easily knocked out by the smallest anti-tank gun, were even employed in the Russian campaign.

The illustrations show both flush-riveted and bolted hull types. Both tanks are shown in desert paint and the colour marking in both cases represents the third tank of the 1st platoon, 1st company of a tank battalion.

13 Lehký Tank LT-35 (Panzerkampfwagen 35(t)), Czechoslovakia.

The Czechoslovak arms industry was one of the strongest in Europe in March 1939 when Czechoslovakia was annexed by Germany. The tanks in particular that were built or being made for the Czechoslovak forces or for export were an extremely useful accession to the new German armoured divisions then being formed.

There were three main centres of tank production in Czechoslovakia: the famous Skoda works at Pilsen; Ceskomoravska-Kolben-Danek (CKD —builders of Praga lorries) at Prague; and Adamov in the Brno region. All three concerns were, however, linked in the exchange of designs and in the sharing of production orders.

The LT-35 was one of the two principal Czechoslovak tank designs when Germany took control of the country. It was a 10-ton tank developed by Skoda from an earlier and lighter model, P.II, apparently originated by CKD, which had been adopted for production by the Czechoslovak army as Lehký Tank (light tank) LT-34. Skoda gave the works designation of S.IIa to the LT.35, which differed from the LT-34 mainly in having thicker armour and a more powerful engine of 120 h.p.—nearly double that of its predecessor. One of its principal features was its relatively simple, rugged design in which more attention than usual was given to ease of operation. A twelve-speed gearbox combined with a pneumatic-servo-mechanical steering unit made the vehicle easy to drive and the suspension, consisting of two four-road-wheel bogie units each side—each unit sprung on a single leaf spring—was exceptionally hard-wearing. An uninterrupted compartment for the four-man crew was achieved by adopting a rear sprocket drive combined with a rear-

engine layout. The armament—common to most of the Czech tanks of this period—consisted of a 37-mm. gun (in this case the Skoda A.3) with a coaxial 7·92-mm. machine-gun which could, if required, be elevated independently. There was a second machine-gun in the hull front.

About 160 LT-35s were built for the Czechoslovak Army and these were taken over by the German Army in 1939. The 6th Panzer Division received 106 of these tanks and these formed the greater part of its equipment for the campaign in the West in May 1940. The LT-35 had not achieved anything like the commercial success of the LT-38 and also was less popular with the Germans than that tank. Production was not continued under German control and after front-line service in the Western campaign, it was phased out of service as a battle tank, although the chassis continued to be used as mortar-carriers or tractors.

The coloured illustrations show a LT-35 in 1939 Czechoslovak Army markings and a PzKpfw 35(t) (as the LT-35 was designated by the German Army) of the 6th Panzer Division in 1940.

14 **Char Léger, Vickers-Carden-Loyd, Modèle T.15,** Belgium.

Belgium relied mainly on French and British equipment for her small mechanised force and several different types of light tracked vehicle were purchased from Vickers-Armstrongs Ltd. in the years leading up to the Second World War.

These British vehicles included versions of the Carden-Loyd Mark VI, both as an anti-tank gun tractor and as a self-propelled mounting for a 47-mm. gun, two other types of armoured tractor mounted with 47-mm. guns (known as T.13 and T.14 to the Belgians), and some light tanks.

The military vehicles offered for sale commercially by Vickers-Armstrongs had, by arrangement with the War Office, to be of different design to those supplied to the British Army. However, the Vickers-Carden-Loyd light tank, 1934 model, purchased by Belgium, had many features in common with the Light Tanks, Marks II, III and IV, of the British Army.

The main features of the Vickers-Carden-Loyd 1934 model were a two-man crew, with engine mounted at the right-hand side of the hull and the turret at the left. The suspension was of the Horstmann type with two two-wheel bogey units each side, controlled by coil springs; front drive sprockets and rear idler wheels. The engine was a Meadows six-cylinder in-line unit of about 90 h.p., used with a five-speed gear-box.

The armament of the Belgian Vickers-Carden-Loyds, which had special turrets, was fitted after delivery and consisted of either a 13·2-mm. Hotchkiss long-barrelled heavy machine-gun or a 20-mm. cannon. Both variants are shown in the illustrations here.

Forty-two machines of this type were delivered to the Belgian Army by the end of 1935. A batch of similar vehicles to the T.15 (the Vickers-Carden-Loyd 1936 model, with one or two machine-guns) was supplied to the Dutch East Indies Army and others were to have been sold to the Dutch

Home Army. The latter were, however, retained in Britain in 1940 and used in the defence of the United Kingdom. An improved model, the so-called Vickers-Carden-Loyd Command Tank with a three-man crew and equipped with a 40-mm. gun, was to have been produced under licence in Belgium, but none had been built there by 1940.

15 Panzerkampfwagen I, Ausf. B, Germany.

Over 500 of these light tanks and of the earlier model PzKpfw IA took part in the campaign in the West in 1940. Before this they had taken an even more prominent part in the Polish campaign. However, it had never been the intention of the German High Command, when these light-machine-gun-armed tanks were put into production, to employ them in major campaigns in this way.

When the expansion and re-equipment of the Reichswehr was decided on in 1932 the main need, initially, was for a supply of tanks that could be built cheaply and issued to the troops for training. For this purpose the firms of Krupp, MAN, Rheinmetall, Henschel and Daimler-Benz were asked to submit prototypes on the lines of the British Vickers-Carden-Loyd light tanks that, by then, had reached a fairly satisfactory state of mechanical development. The Krupp design known as L.K.A.1 was selected as the first production model in 1934, eventually becoming known as, PzKpfw IA. A second prototype, L.K.B.1, in which a more powerful engine (a Maybach Krupp air-cooled model) replaced the original Krupp air-cooled type, was also put into production as PzKpfw I, Ausf. B.

The earliest versions to appear of both these models had open-top hulls and no turrets. This, and the designation—landwirtschaftliche Schlepper (La.S.) (agricultural tractor)—was intended to disguise their true purpose, although in this form they were still entirely suitable for driver training and tactical exercises.

The layout of both the A and the B models was the same—a rear-mounted engine with the transmission led forward to front driving sprockets. The crew compartment was in the centre of the vehicle, with the driver at the left. The turret, mounting two machine-guns, was off-set to the right on the roof of the hull. In the suspension the front road wheel was sprung independently on a coil spring and the remaining wheels in pairs on leaf springs linked by a girder for extra rigidity. In the PzKpfw IB an extra road wheel was added each side to carry the lengthened hull made necessary by the larger engine.

Production of the PzKpfw IA was limited to about 500, but nearly 2,000 of the IB, which was the much more important model, were built. In 1936 both types were tried out in combat in the Spanish Civil War when the shortcomings of a two-man crew and the lack of an anti-tank gun were brought out. By 1939 sufficient tanks of more powerful type had not been built to replace them, and for this reason they had to be used both in Poland and the following year in France. A few were still in service even in the campaign in Russia in 1941.

16 **Char Léger F.C.M.36,** France.

Built by Forges et Chantiers de la Mediterrannée in conjunction with Automobiles M. Berliet (which provided the engine) the FCM 36 came into production in 1936 to help increase the supply of tanks for the French infantry-support units. As such, it was a tank in the same broad specification as the more widely known Renault R.35, but the FCM 36 had some unusual features for French tanks of its time and some of these were in advance of developments elsewhere.

Of fairly conventional general layout, the FCM 36 had the engine at the rear, driving rear sprockets, but it was uncommon in that this was a diesel (of Ricardo design and built by Berliet under licence). Only two other French tanks produced around this time (the AMX 38 and B1 ter) shared this feature, which gave the FCM 36 a range of 200 miles—double that of most of its contemporaries in the French Army.

The armour protection was to the 40-mm. maximum standard required of French infantry tanks of this period, but another rare feature for the time was that for both hull and turret welded construction was used—an achievement which anticipated the method of welding armour plate in the United Kingdom, for example, by several years. The angles of the armour plate were (except for the suspension skirting plates) well thought out and the flat surfaces were able to offer the same sort of protection as the rounded cast armour that was used in most other French infantry tanks. The armament was one 37-mm. gun and one 7·5-mm. machine-gun.

Only 100 FMC 36s were built and this number, allowing for reserves, was sufficient for the equipment of two units—4e and 7e Bataillons de Chars de Combat.

17 Light Tank 7TP, Poland.

About forty Vickers-Armstrongs 6-ton tanks were purchased from England between 1932 and 1934. These tanks were widely popular in the 1930s and they were sold to many countries at this time. They were of a straightforward but effective design and it was decided to build them in Poland in a slightly modified form, which became known as 7TP.

The Vickers-Armstrongs tanks appeared in two versions, one with two turrets armed with two machine-guns, and the other with a single turret mounting a gun and a single machinegun. The 7TP also appeared in two versions at first, but the later production models, incorporating improvements, were built only in the singleturret version. The final model, in production up to 1939, is shown in the illustrations. This type had the normal Vickers suspension but incorporated a special Polish turret (built in Sweden) with a 37-mm. gun and a coaxial machine-gun. The general appearance was much the same as the Vickers-built tanks, but a 110-h.p. Saurer-designed diesel engine was used in place of the 80-h.p. air-cooled petrol engines of the former. This helped to maintain a similar performance to that of the earlier tanks although the armour had, in the final Polish model, been increased to a maximum of 40 mm. on the hull and 30 mm. on the turret.

Approximately 170 7TPs of all types were built (in addition to the Vicker tanks bought from England) and they formed the backbone of the Polish armoured forces in September 1939. Somewhat old-fashioned compared with the German tanks against which they were opposed, the 7TPs were nevertheless better in armament than the PzKpfw Is and IIs which formed the bulk of the German armour.

18 Medium Tank 10TP, Poland.

This interesting tank, which existed only in prototype form, was a Polish version of the Christie model 1931 medium tank. Five vehicles of this type were ordered from J. Walter Christie for the United States Army together with two for the Polish Government. Two further chassis, together with the manufacturing licence, were sold to the U.S.S.R. and these formed the basis of the BT ('fast tank') series which was eventually developed into the T-34.

The Polish Government defaulted on their order for the two Christie tanks and these vehicles were, accordingly, delivered to the U.S. Army where they were designated Medium Tanks T.3E1. However, the knowledge gained by the Poles from examination of Christie's prototypes and specifications was put to good use, because a prototype tank was built in 1936–7 which closely resembled the T3.E1.

The main characteristics of the Christie design were high speed, attained by means of a high power/weight ratio and an effective suspension system, and the ability to run on wheels as well as tracks. These features were reproduced in the 10TP, the Polish version, in which the engine was a German twelve-cylinder Maybach of 300 h.p., giving a reported speed of 31 m.p.h. on tracks and 47 m.p.h. on wheels.

The suspension was of the normal Christie type with four large road wheels each side, each wheel independently sprung on a leading or trailing arm, controlled by a long coil spring, all the springs being contained between the inner and outer skins of the side armour. For running on wheels, the tracks were removed and the second pair of road wheels was raised. The front pair of road wheels was steerable and the transmission was transferred from the rear drive sprockets to the rear road wheels.

The armament of the 10TP prototype consisted of a 37-mm. gun and a coaxial machine-gun in a turret which was identical to that of the contemporary version of the 7TP—a light tank already in service with the Polish Army. In addition there was a second machine-gun in the front of the hull. Armour was on a maximum of 20 mm. for the hull and 16 mm. for the turret.

A battalion of 10TP tanks was intended to form the main fighting element in each of the Polish motorised cavalry brigades, the formation of which began in 1937. Two of these brigades were in existence on 1 September 1939, but without their 10TPs, since production of this tank had not been started, and so it never had the opportunity of being tested in action.

19 Schwere Panzerspähwagen (6-rad) SdKfz 231 and 232, Germany.

The six-wheeled German armoured cars in service in 1939–40 and used in the campaigns in Poland and the West were the product of experiments begun ten years earlier with standard six-wheeled lorry chassis.

In the late twenties, the most effective way of obtaining a reasonable cross-country performance without excessive cost was to use a six-wheeled lorry with drive transmitted to all four rear wheels. The commercial vehicle manufacturers of Daimler-Benz, Büssing and C. D. Magirus all made available chassis of this type and, with some modifications, including duplicate steering controls at the rear, all three types were produced as armoured cars. The armoured hulls in the first vehicles of the three makes differed from each other but eventually a standardised form was developed with only slight modifications (such as the bonnet length and form of radiator protection) for each chassis manufacturer. The armoured hulls were supplied by Deutsche Edelstahl of Hanover and Deutsche Werke of Kiel and were ballistically much in advance of those of most British armoured cars of the period.

The chassis were conventional with front-mounted engine and drive transmitted to the rear bogie (all the rear wheels were dual): suspension was by means of longitudinal leaf springs. The engines were petrol units of between 65 and 70 h.p.: six-cylinder in the case of the Daimler-Benz and Magirus and four-cylinder for the Büssing.

One disadvantage of six-wheeled chassis of this kind with a relatively long wheel-base was that the underside of the body between the front and rear wheels was liable to ground when going across rough country. To counter this tendency, the Magirus models (which were the last in production) had a roller added midway between the front wheels and the leading pair of rear wheels.

Sufficient of these cars were produced to re-equip the German Army and they performed useful service in pre-war training and exercises and even in the campaigns of 1939–40. Their deficiencies in performance were well realised, however, and from about 1938 onwards they were progressively replaced by their eight-wheeled counterparts.

The six-wheeled armoured cars were built in three versions: SdKfz 231—the normal gun car, armed with one 2-cm. gun and one machine-gun; SdKfz 232—similar to SdKfz 231, but with the addition of a frame wireless aerial; SdKfz 263 Panzerfunkwagen—a command vehicle with a non-rotating turret with one machine-gun only and having a crew increased to five men instead of four.

20 Panzerkampfwagen II, Ausf. c, Germany.

The plans for the re-equipment of the Reichswehr were based on medium tanks armed with shell-firing guns. These were expensive and took longer to produce than light tanks, however, and it was decided to build a 10-ton tank as an interim measure to supplement the 6-ton PzKpfw I models. An upward step was the 2-cm. cannon included in the armament specification and the command position was considerably improved by the addition of a third man to the crew.

Prototype vehicles to the new specification were completed by MAN, Henschel and Krupp—in 1934—and of these the MAN version was chosen for production. The first model of this appeared in 1935 as PzKpfw II, Ausf. a1, followed in small numbers by Ausf. a2, a3 and b which had successive improvements in engine cooling and suspension. All these earlier models had a suspension system somewhat similar to that of PzKpfw I. In the next model, Ausf. c, an entirely different form of suspension was introduced and this, together with the more powerful 6·2-litre engine (used first in Ausf. b), gave this model a far better performance than its predecessors and created the basis of the design for most of its successors.

The Ausf. c., like the earlier models, had a rear-mounted engine and transmission through driving sprockets at the front, but the suspension consisted of five medium-sized road wheels each side, each sprung independently on leaf springs.

The PzKpfw II was employed in Poland in 1939 and in France in 1940, when the Ausf. c formed an important element. Nine hundred and fifty-five PzKpfw IIs were in service at the beginning of the Western Campaign. They could be said to have formed the backbone of the panzer troops because they represented the highest number of any one type out of the 2,500 German tanks used.

21 BA-32 (Armoured Car), U.S.S.R.

The only heavy armoured car to be employed by the U.S.S.R. in the Second World War, the BA-32 was a direct successor—and easily recognisable as such —to the BA-10 which first went into mass production in 1930. Very typical of their era (armoured cars of similar type were built in Britain, Germany and the U.S.A.), the BA-10 and BA-32 were built on GAZ six-wheeled lorry chassis, the GAZ being a Russian version of a Ford design. The use of a normal front-engined chassis of this kind largely dictated the armoured car layout, so that the driver was behind the engine, with a co-driver's machine-gun position beside him, and the turret was located over the rear wheels. The turrets used in this BA-10/BA-32 series were those of contemporary tanks and the armament ranged from a 37-mm. gun and coaxial machine-gun, in early versions, to the 45-mm. gun and machine-gun in the version (BA-32-2) shown in the illustrations. The armoured hull was of riveted construction in the early versions, but welding later came increasingly into use and in the final version the hull sides were more sloping and the roof at the rear was lowered, together with the turret, so that the 45-mm. gun only just cleared the part of the hull over the driver's head.

To improve its performance over snow or soft ground the rear wheels of the BA-32 could be fitted with tracks, as shown in one of the illustrations.

22 Tank, Vickers 6-ton (T-26E), Finland.

Finland was among the many countries that tested various models of Vickers and Vickers-Carden-Loyd tanks offered for sale commercially by Vickers-Armstrongs Ltd. in the 1930s. This led to an order for sixteen Vickers 6-ton tanks which were delivered in 1938,

followed by a further sixteen in 1939.

These tanks, powered by a four-cylinder 90-h.p. Armstrong Siddeley engine, were of the single-turret variation known as 'Alternative B' to the manufacturers. The standard armament was a 47-mm. gun. However, a proportion of those used by the Finns had machine-guns only and others were fitted in 1939 with a special mounting for the French Puteaux 37-mm. gun, of the type used in the old Renault FT tanks acquired by the Finns in 1919. One 6-ton tank was modified in 1940 to receive a Swedish Bofors 37-mm. gun and mounting of the pattern found in some models of the Swedish Landsverk six-wheeled armoured car, one of which had been bought by Finland in 1939. These three variants of the Vickers 6-ton tank were unique and used only by the Finns.

During the Russo-Finnish war in 1939-40 and again in 1941 quantities of Russian tanks were captured and taken into service with the Finnish Army. The most numerous of these were T-26s, the Russian-built version of the Vickers 6-ton tank. The Russian tanks, apart from their armament, were almost unchanged in design and were readily absorbed into new Finnish tank units. Eventually, the original Vickers 6-ton tanks from England were designated T-26E by the Finns.

23 BT-7 ('Fast Tank'), U.S.S.R.

The most important Soviet tank numerically in 1939, the BT-7 was the last in a series developed from an almost exact copy of the American Christie M-1931 tank.

Two Christie tanks were imported

from the United States in 1931 and given searching tests in the U.S.S.R. which were obviously satisfactory, because they were followed by the manufacture, in a remarkably short time, of the first vehicles built under licence. They were adapted slightly and simplified to meet Soviet production requirements but even the power plant—a Liberty V twelve-cylinder modified aero engine—was built in the U.S.S.R. After use in service, the series was developed through a number of models (not all of which went beyond the drawing board or prototype vehicles) up to the BT-7, which first went into production in 1935. The type had the special Russian classification of Bystrochodnij Tank ('Fast Tank').

Although superior to earlier models in engine power, armour and armament, the BT-7 retained the salient Christie features of high speed, both on and off tracks, and good cross-country running ability. These characteristics were due mainly to the high power/weight ratio of over 30 h.p./ton and the Christie suspension system, consisting of four large-diameter road wheels each side, indepently mounted at the end of leading or trailing swing arms, controlled by long coil springs. The springs were mounted between the inner and outer hull side plates. Transmission from the engine mounted at the rear was to track-drive sprockets at the back. When the tracks were removed and the tank converted to run on wheels (a process which took about half an hour) the drive was transferred from the rear sprockets to the rear road wheel on each side. In this configuration the front two road wheels were used for steering instead of the clutch and brake system employed when on tracks. On wheels, the BT-7 had a top speed of 45 m.p.h., but even on tracks the maximum was 33 m.p.h.

The BT-7 in its later standardised form had armament consisting of a 45-mm. gun and a coaxial 7·62-mm. machine-gun. In some cases, there was a second machine-gun in a ball mounting in the rear of the turret, which was mainly of welded construction. Earlier models, however (like the BT-7-1, shown on wheels in one of the illustrations), retained the older cylindrical riveted turret of the BT-5. The original Liberty engine had, on the BT-7, been replaced by a 450-h.p. twelve-cylinder V-type of different design.

Still in service in large numbers at the time of the German invasion in 1941, tanks of the BT series were by then too lightly armoured and were as soon as possible replaced by T-34s, a type which owed a great deal to them.

24 STZ Komsomolets (Armoured Tractor), U.S.S.R.

The Russians were one of the few countries to produce and put into service before the Second World War a similar type of vehicle to the British tracked carrier series. Although intended primarily as an artillery tractor, the STZ most closely resembled the configuration of the British Cavalry Carrier which also had an armoured driver's and machine-gunner's compartment at the front and longitudinal outward-facing seats at the rear for the crew, unprotected by armour. An overhead frame sometimes fitted in the

STZ served both as a wireless aerial and to carry a canvas roof for the rear compartment.

Weighing just over 4 tons and with a maximum speed of 25 m.p.h., the STZ was used as a tractor for anti-tank guns or light infantry howitzers, or as an ammunition carrier. First appearing in 1937 and seeing use in the Finnish campaign in 1939–40 and the opening stages of the German attack against Russia in 1941, the STZ was succeeded as a gun tractor by later tracked, semi-tracked or wheeled vehicles of both Russian and American manufacture. However, STZ chassis only slightly modified were used as a self-propelled mounting for the 57-mm. anti-tank gun and this equipment was in service as late as mid-1942.

25 Carrier, Bren, U.K.

The tracked armoured carrier was one of the most characteristic vehicles of the British Army in the Second World War and around 50,000 of all types were built in the United Kingdom alone by 1945, similar vehicles being also made in quantity in Canada and the U.S.A. as well as in other Commonwealth countries.

One of the earliest types of carrier to be used in the Second World War was the Carrier, Bren, but although in this particular form relatively few were built (then being replaced by the Carrier, Universal) the name Bren Carrier continued in popular usage for all types throughout the war.

Built as a larger and more sophisticated replacement for the Carden-Loyd Mark VI, the new Carrier for the transport of infantry machine guns was evolved by Vickers-Armstrongs Ltd. from their series of Light Dragon artillery tractors. The prototype Carrier, M.G., for the Vickers 0·303-in. machine-gun, appeared in 1935 and, after trials, a pilot batch was ordered in 1936, followed in the same year by a first larger production contract. Further contracts were awarded in 1937 and the later vehicles of some of these orders were completed as Carriers, Bren, in which the mounting was adapted for the new 0·303-in. Bren light machine-gun which was just coming into service with the infantry.

The most interesting feature of the Bren Carrier (and all other carriers of the same mechanical design) was the steering system. This was operated by a steering wheel (with the consequent advantage of simplification of driver training during the expansion of the Army). When the steering wheel was turned, the front two-wheel suspension units on each side were moved laterally, being mounted on a cross-tube which ran through the vehicle. This bowed the tracks into a curve, which the vehicle followed. Further movement of the steering wheel operated track brakes on either side, causing a skid turn.

The suspension consisted, each side, of two road wheels in one Horstmann-type bogie unit, sprung on a pair of oblique coil springs, and a single wheel unit of generally similar type. The idler wheel was at the front. Power was provided by a 65-h.p. Ford V-8 engine in the first vehicles, although later 85-h.p. Canadian or U.S.-built engines were also used.

The crew of the Carrier, Bren, consisted of three men, the driver at the right and the gunner beside him at the left with an extension of the armour in front of him to facilitate operation of the Bren gun when mounted in the vehicle (normally it was intended that the gun should be operated from the ground in normal infantry fashion). The third man sat behind the gunner in a separate compartment and the armour was extended rearwards on this side to protect him. The maximum armour thickness of the Carrier was 12 mm.

Bren Carriers were used in all the campaigns of the British Army in the earlier years of the Second World War, before being replaced by Carriers, Universal.

One illustration shows a Carrier, Bren, No. 2, Mark II (the No. 2 indicates a U.S.-built engine, the Mark number indicating slight changes in the hull), from above in colours used in France in 1940. The other view is of a Carrier belonging to the 2nd Battalion The Cameronians, of the 4th Indian Division in the Middle East in 1940.

26 Carrier, Cavalry, Mark I and Carrier, Scout, Mark I, U.K.

The Carrier, Cavalry, was conceived as a vehicle for mechanised cavalry in a new role in which the troopers could be carried forward with their weapons, dismount rapidly and go into action. The chassis that was already in production as a M.G. Carrier was selected for conversion for this function. The front part of the armoured hull, including the gunner's compartment and gun-mounting, was retained, only slightly modified. At the rear, however, longitudinal seats were provided each side for the cavalrymen. There was also

a curved guard over the tracks to protect the men's legs, a folding handrail each side and provision for an overhead canvas hood. There was no armour protection for the passengers at the rear. Only fifty Cavalry Carriers were built (by Nuffield Mechanisations Ltd.) and although some were taken to France by the British Expeditionary Force and employed as personnel carriers, the role for which they were designed was by then realised to be impractical in modern warfare.

The Scout Carrier also was designed as a vehicle principally for the cavalry, although in this case it was anticipated that the weapons carried would be used from the vehicle to a greater extent, and all-round protection was provided for all the crew. Again, the basic M.G. or Bren Carrier chassis was adapted, the front being almost identical except that the gunner's compartment was intended for the mounting of a 0·55-in. Boys anti-tank rifle. The third man of the crew was situated at the right-hand side, behind the driver, and in his compartment was carried a 0·303-in. Bren machine-gun on a mounting suitable for use against air or ground targets. To complete the armament, a 3-in. smoke discharger (similar to that carried on the light tanks with which these carriers often operated) was mounted on the right-hand side of the hull. A No. 2 wireless set was carried at the back of the rear compartment in some vehicles. Six hundred and sixty-seven Scout Carriers were built and used by the divisional cavalry regiments of infantry divisions in 1939-40 and also by motor battalions of armoured divisions in both Europe and the Middle East.

The illustration of a Carrier, Scout, Mark I, shows a vehicle belonging to the 13th/18th Royal Hussars, the divisional cavalry regiment of the 1st Infantry Division with the British Expeditionary Force in France. The view of a Cavalry Carrier shows the framework for the canvas roof in position.

27 Armoured Car, Reconnaissance, Morris (Model CS9/LAC), U.K.

Built on a modified Morris Commercial 15-cwt 4 × 2 truck chassis, this armoured car was, in effect, a stop-gap design to replace older six-wheeled armoured cars pending the development of new four-wheel-drive chassis.

After the prototype was tested in 1936, a further ninety-nine vehicles with slight modifications were ordered and these were delivered about 1938. Thirty-eight cars of this kind were taken to France by the 12th Royal Lancers, the only armoured car regiment with the British Expeditionary Force, and later, thirty were issued to the 11th Hussars in Egypt, by whom they were used in conjunction with some 1920 and 1924 pattern Rolls-Royce armoured cars, rearmed. A high performance cross-country was not expected of vehicles with conventional 4 × 2 transmission, but the 11th Hussars found that the Morris armoured cars (which were fitted with desert tyres) traversed soft sand better than the Rolls-Royce, though the springs and steering did not stand up so well.

The Morris CS9/LAC had a six-cylinder engine of 96·2 h.p., which gave it a top speed of 45 m.p.h. The armament consisted of a 0·55-in. Boys anti-tank rifle and a 0·303-in. Bren light machine-gun mounted independently in an open-topped turret. The crew consisted of four men—commander, gunner, driver and wireless operator (who sat beside the driver).

The 12th Royal Lancers' cars did useful work in protecting the flank of the British Expeditionary Force before the evacuation from Dunkirk, when they were left behind in France. The 11th Hussars used their Morris armoured cars in North Africa up to the Spring of 1941, although by this time some had been converted into light armoured command vehicles.

The illustrations show a car ('Cowes') of C Squadron, the 12th Royal Lancers and a car of the 11th Hussars as it appeared in the Western Desert campaign.

28 Schwere Panzerspähwagen (8-rad) SdKf2 231 and 232, Germany.

The six-wheeled armoured cars produced in the 1930s for the German Army were accepted only for their relative cheapness as a means of speeding rearmament. When the time came to consider replacements for them, however, it was natural to turn for inspiration to the very advanced experimental multi-wheeled armoured cars which had preceded the six-wheelers.

The new eight-wheeled armoured car series was developed, commencing in 1935, by the Büssing-NAG firm which had built a ten-wheeled prototype in 1929. Büssing had also, of course, produced a proportion of the chassis for the six-wheeled armoured cars and these had provided a useful fund of knowledge of operational requirements.

A rear-engined layout with transmission to all eight wheels, all of which steered, was adopted for the new armoured car chassis. This made for a highly complicated transmission and steering linkage arrangement, but produced a cross-country performance as good as that of a tracked vehicle and, for an armoured car of this size (about 19 ft long), fairly good manoeuvrability. A second driver's position, with controls, was provided at the rear. The suspension consisted of a pair of longitudinal leaf springs for each 'bogie' unit of four wheels.

The armoured hull of the SdKfz 231 (8-rad) was of very similar shape (although turned round) to that of the six-wheeled armoured cars, which had proved to be of a satisfactory ballistic design. The turret was also much the same in general appearance, although the face was cleaned up and the machine-gun was transferred to the left of the 2-cm. gun. The corresponding wireless-equipped version, SdKfz 232, employed a generally similar, although simplified, frame aerial to that of the wireless six-wheeler. Only in the third basic model, the SdKfz 263 (8-rad) command vehicle, was there a wider departure from previous practice, in that the turret was dispensed with completely and the crew compartment enlarged and extended in height to accommodate five men, including a formation commander and members of his staff.

For their size the eight-wheelers of the SdKfz 231 series were only lightly armoured and armed, the emphasis being on mobility. The armour plate thicknesses were, in fact, no more than comparable with those of the German light 4 × 4 armoured cars, although

an extra spaced plate was added in some cases to the eight-wheelers.

The SdKfz 231 and 232 eight-wheelers were first delivered to the troops in 1938 and so some were in service in the Polish Campaign the following year (one of these, of an SS unit, is shown in one illustration) and in greater numbers in the Western Campaign. As the war progressed they replaced entirely the six-wheelers in front-line units.

29 Schwerer geländegängiger gepanzerter Personenkraftwagen, SdKfz 247, Germany.

Bearing the cumbersome designation of 'heavy cross-country armoured personnel car' (sch. gl. gp. Pkw.), this type of vehicle was an armoured staff car for very senior officers and was, accordingly, produced only in very limited numbers.

The original version was built in 1937–8 on the Krupp 6 × 4 chassis, type L2H143, which had a four-cylinder engine of about 60 h.p. with a four-speed gearbox. About twenty were made and these were supplemented in 1939 by a similar number of vehicles built on the Horch 'standard chassis II for heavy passenger cars'. This chassis was used for a variety of unarmoured military vehicles and was similar in many respects to that used for the four-wheeled armoured cars of the SdKfz 221–223 series except that the engine was mounted at the front instead of the rear. The eight-cylinder engine was rated at about 80 h.p. and was used with a five-speed gearbox. Transmission was on all four wheels.

The armoured bodies for both six-wheeled and four-wheeled cars were similar in design and of roughly the same overall dimensions and they accommodated six men, including the driver. The armoured protection was on an 8-mm. basis.

30 Panzerkampfwagen 38(t) (LT-38), Czechoslovakia.

One of the most successful products of the pre-Second World War Czechoslovak armaments industry, the LT-38 or closely similar versions of it were sold to over half a dozen different countries.

The design of the LT-38 originated with Ceskomoravska-Kolben-Danek of Prague in 1933 with a model known as LTL. This model was progressively improved and in 1938 150 of the current version, TNHP, were ordered for the Czechoslovak Army. In the meantime, different variants of the design had been sold to a number of countries and export orders, including those for the TNHP, eventually totalled nearly 200, a not inconsiderable number for peacetime sales. The tank was purchased mostly by smaller countries as wide apart as Peru and Sweden.

Exports ceased when Germany annexed Czechoslovakia in March 1939, although Sweden was permitted to build them under licence. One TNHP was sold to the United Kingdom and tested by the Mechanical Warfare Experimental Establishment in 1939. Their report was mildly favourable but the tank was regarded as cramped and uncomfortable for the crew. The German Army, on the other hand, considered the LT-38 to be a good tank and were extremely glad to be able to take over all the existing stocks, both of the Czechoslovak Army and those intended for export. Production was continued and increased under German control and LT-38s, redesignated PzKpfw 38(t), were soon issued to the 7th Panzer Division (commanded by Rommel) and 8th Panzer Division, both formed in October 1939. Two hundred and twenty-eight PzKpfw 38(t)s (most of them in 7th and 8th Panzer Divisions) were available at the opening of the campaign in the West in May 1940, but by 1941 this type of tank formed about 25% of the total tank strength of the Wehrmacht.

The LT-38 was built to a layout that has since become fairly commonplace but was by no means so widespread when its design commenced in 1933. The engine (a Praga six-cylinder type) was in a compartment at the rear with the transmission carried forward through the crew compartment to the pre-selection five-speed gearbox near the front of the vehicle. In front of the gearbox was the cross shaft incorporating the steering clutches carrying the drive to the tracks via front sprockets. The suspension appeared externally to be of the Christie type but was in fact of the semi-elliptic leaf spring variety, one spring controlling a pair of road wheels each side.

The turret, mounted on the roof of the fighting compartment, was centrally placed and carried a 37-mm. gun (Skoda model A7) and a 7·92-mm. machine-gun. Another machine-gun was mounted in the front of the hull at the left-hand side, next to the driver who could, if necessary, fire this weapon by means of a Bowden cable connected to one of the steering levers.

Good general features of the LT-38 were its sturdiness, reliability and ease of maintenance. The Germans felt it worth keeping in production (with some improvements) until 1942, when 1,168 had been produced. Although by then outclassed as a gun-tank, the chassis continued to be produced for various German self-propelled mountings until the end of the war. The tanks sold abroad or produced under licence continued in service until well after the war in some countries.

Both illustrations show PzKpfw 38(t)s in German service.

31 Porte-Pont, Somua-Coder MSCL-5, France.

This interesting vehicle was designed not long before the outbreak of the Second World War by the Société Coder de Marseille to provide a quick means of placing a bridge under fire over small rivers or similar obstacles. The bridge was about 27 ft long and could take light and medium tanks up to around 22 tons.

The bridge was carried upside down over the top of the carrying vehicle and pivoted at the rear. When laying the bridge, the vehicle was backed up to the edge of the river and the bridge raised by a hydraulic ram. As the bridge moved through the beginning of its arc of about 180 degrees, its weight was taken by two quadrant-shaped supports which moved down into contact with the ground. When the bridge had completed its arc and was resting on the other side of the river it was released from the carrying vehicle.

The whole process could be carried out by the crew under cover, the carrying vehicle, a Somua half-track,

being fully protected with bullet-proof plate.

32 T-28C (Medium Tank), U.S.S.R.

Believed to have been inspired by contemporary British and German designs (the A.6 Medium and the so-called 'Gross traktor' series, respectively) the T-28 was the first Russian-built medium tank to be accepted for service with the Red Army.

Designed at the Kirov Plant at Leningrad, the first prototype of the T-28 was tested during 1932. After modifications this model was put into production. Development was continued through several models and manufacture was continued until 1939 with the final standard model, T-28C, which is shown in the illustrations.

The T-28C shared the same layout and characteristics of the earlier models, but a newer, more powerful version of the 76·2-mm. main gun (of calibre L/26) was used. Also included in the main turret was a machine-gun in a ball mounting. The two auxiliary turrets, one either side of the driver, had one machine-gun each so that in the frontal assaults for which the T-28 was intended, a bewildering volume of fire could be maintained. The frontal armour of the T-28C was likewise improved, to a maximum of 80 mm, although it is likely that this was of limited distribution.

The driver's and fighting compartments of the T-28 (occupied by the crew of six) were in the front half of the tank and the engine compartment was at the rear, the transmission being to rear drive sprockets. The engine used was the M-17L (a Russian version of the American Liberty aero engine) twelve-cylinder V—of 500 h.p.: this gave a top speed of about 20 m.p.h.

Although the specification of the T-28 does not appear bad on paper, the design was found to be inadequate even in the Finnish campaign and when in 1941 these tanks came up against German armour their tall silhouette (with auxiliary turrets which were virtually useless in open warfare) and relatively thin rear and side armour made them easy victims.

33 T-35 (Heavy Tank), U.S.S.R.

This imposing but thinly-armoured heavy tank was one of the last manifestations of the fashion set by the British A1.E1 'Independent' tank of 1926.

The idea behind the A1.E1 was that by providing the tank with a multiplicity of turrets, so that fire could be brought to bear on all sides at once, combined with mobility, independent missions could be undertaken without support by other arms. Although Russian tactical ideas may not necessarily have coincided with those of the British, a Soviet tank on the same theme as the A1.E1 (which was experimental only) was put into service about 1931. This was the T-32 and it was followed in 1933 by the T-35, which continued in production until 1939, although a total of only twenty to thirty was built.

Like its British progenitor, the T-35 had five turrets; a large turret mounting the main armament and four subsidiary turrets grouped round it. The main turret mounted a 76·2-mm gun. and one machine-gun in a ball mounting in the turret face; two of the

auxiliary turrets (the front right and rear left) mounted 45-mm. guns and the other two small turrets had one machine-gun each. Early versions of the tank had 37-mm. guns instead of 45-mm. and there were various modifications to the armament (sometimes involving the removal of the two machine-gun turrets) in the later years of the T-35's existence. Armour protection was to a front hull maximum of 30 mm. on early models and 35 mm. on later versions.

Powered by a 500-h.p. twelve-cylinder V model M-17 M engine situated in the rear half of the hull, the 45-ton T-35 had a maximum road speed of 18 m.p.h. The cross-country speed was given as 12 m.p.h. and it is likely that, because of its length (32 ft), this could be maintained by the T-35 better than most of its contemporaries. The clutch and brake steering system was said to have been unsatisfactory, however.

Tanks of this type were used in the 1939 Finnish campaign, where they were not very successful, and a number were also intended for use against the Germans in Poland in 1941 where, however, they ran out of fuel before being engaged.

The illustrations show the second model of the T-35, fitted with a frame wireless aerial on the turret.

34 Pansarbil m/39-40, Sweden.

Known by its manufacturers as the Landsverk Lynx, this armoured car was of advanced conception when it first appeared in 1938 and it still appears modern more than thirty years later.

A vehicle of nearly symmetrical profile, the Lynx was armed with a 20-mm. gun and a coaxial 8-mm. air-cooled machine-gun in the turret and two further 8-mm. machine-guns in the front and the rear of the hull respectively. The car had the large crew of six men, three of them gunners.

The engine of the Landsverk Lynx was a six-cylinder Volvo of 135 h.p. which gave a top speed of 44 m.p.h. Transmission was to all four wheels, which on early vehicles, like some previous Landsverk armoured cars, were of resilient rubber but not pneumatic. However, later cars had pneumatic tyres.

35 Stridsvagn m/39, Sweden.

The Swedish armaments industry is probably better known for its artillery than for its armoured fighting vehicles. There has, nevertheless, been a history of the steady development of tanks and armoured cars dating back to 1921 and in this work the AB Landsverk concern has taken a leading part.

A version of the German L.K. I light tank of the First World War was built in Sweden in 1921 and its designer, Josef Vollmer, subsequently designed the Landsverk 10 which was the first of a new series of light and medium tanks which, with successive improvements, continued in production well into the Second World War. Some of these were sold abroad and others were used at home by the Swedish Army.

The latest of this Landsverk series in 1939 was the Landsverk L-60D, a 9-ton tank armed with a 37-mm. gun which was adopted by the Swedish Army as Stridsvagn m/39. Developed from its immediate predecessor (Strv. m/38), the L-60D differed externally in that it

had the unusual armament of twin 8-mm. air-cooled machine-guns mounted in the turret coaxially with the 37-mm. gun.

The engine was a six-cylinder Scania Vabis of 142 h.p. mounted at the rear and driving front sprockets and the steering was a geared system developed from patents taken out by Landsverk in 1930/1. A torsion-bar suspension was used for the four medium-sized road wheels each side, with a trailing idler wheel of the same size at the rear.

In 1941 the Strv. m/39 was succeeded by the Strv. m/40, which was improved in that it had the conventional gearbox replaced by a hydraulic pre-selector box coupled to a low-range mechanical gearbox for cross-country work. The only external difference from the Strv. m/39 was the addition to the turret of a cupola with armoured episcopes.

36 T-26B (Light Tank), U.S.S.R.

The T-26 was the Russian-built version of the Vickers-Armstrongs 6-ton Tank, fifteen of which were ordered from the United Kingdom in 1930. The original Vickers tank was available in two models, one with two turrets, side by side, and the other with a single large turret. The original T-26s built under licence were almost identical to their British-made prototypes. Both twin- and single-turret versions were manufactured in the Soviet Union, but from about 1933 onwards development of the 6-ton type of tank was concentrated on the single-turret model, in which a larger gun could be installed.

Production of the T-26 ran through

until 1939, the final standard version being the T-26S (usually known outside the U.S.S.R. as T-26C). This differed externally from earlier models in the increased use of welded armour, with sloping hull plates and a turret of more streamlined appearance than hitherto. Turrets of this later type were in some cases used to replace those of earlier pattern on earlier models of the T-26, and T-26Bs with the new turret are shown in the illustrations.

Apart from this relatively minor change, the T-26 remained both in mechanical specification and general appearance very close to its prototype, the Vickers-Armstrongs 6-ton tank. The engine, an Armstrong-Siddeley eight-cylinder 90-h.p., air-cooled type, built under licence, was situated at the rear, the transmission being led forwards to drive front sprockets. The gearbox (beside the driver's feet) had five forward speeds and steering was of the clutch and brake type. The suspension was of the simple robust type designed by Vickers and consisted of two groups of four bogie wheels each side, sprung on quarter-elliptic leaf springs. The crew compartment was in the centre of the vehicle with the driver at the right and the turret on the roof.

In its armament the T-26B and later Soviet models was greatly improved over the Vickers 6-ton in that the short 47-mm. gun was replaced by a long 45-mm. L/46 gun of much higher velocity. There was also a co-axial machine-gun and in some cases a second machine-gun in the turret rear.

T-26s of all models were an important factor in the building up of the tank strength of the U.S.S.R. in the 1930s, and although mass production ceased in 1939, they were used in action against the Finns in 1939–40 and even against the Germans in 1941, although phased out of service soon afterwards.

37 Tank, Light, M2A4, U.S.A.

In 1939 the latest of a line of light tanks developed from 1933 onwards, the M2A4 was the first to carry a 37-mm. gun. This light tank also had the distinction of being one of the very earliest types of fighting vehicle to be supplied to Britain by the U.S.A., a small batch being shipped in 1941.

Powered by a 250-h.p. seven-cylinder Continental radial engine (a modified aero engine), giving a top speed of 37 m.p.h., armoured to a 25.4-mm. maximum and equipped with the 37-mm. gun, which was not greatly inferior to the British 2-pr as an armour-piercing weapon, the M2A4 was much better than contemporary British light tanks and comparable with some cruiser tanks. The secondary armament, in addition to the turret coaxial 0·30-in. Browning machine-gun, included two further Brownings in sponsons at either side of the driver's and co-driver's positions and another in the glacis plate. Some or all of these hull-mounted machine-guns were often removed in the tanks in British service.

The suspension consisted of two two-wheeled bogie units each side, each unit sprung on vertical volute springs. The idler wheel was at the rear, off the ground, and the drive sprocket at the front.

A total of 365 M2A4s was built. A few were used in action with U.S.

forces in the Pacific theatre in 1942. Those delivered to Britain in 1941 (only about forty or so) were used for Home Defence and training, in which role they were useful for familiarising the troops with the similar but improved M3 Light Tank.

The illustrations show an M2A4 supplied to Britain that was subscribed for by the Canadian town of Saskatoon, and an M2A4 of the U.S. 70th Armoured Regiment.

38 Scout Car, M3A1, U.S.A.

Designed as a reconnaissance vehicle for the U.S. mechanised cavalry, the M3A1 Scout Car, built by the White Motor Company, was the last in line of a series of vehicles developed from 1929 onwards. A large, open-topped armoured vehicle, with protection ranging from 6 mm. to 12 mm., the M3A1 was powered by a 110-h.p. Hercules six-cylinder engine which gave it a maximum speed of 55-60 m.p.h. Sufficient petrol was carried for a range of 250 miles and cross-country performance with four-wheel drive was fairly good: a roller mounted at the front assisted in surmounting obstacles.

Introduced into service with the U.S. Army in mid 1939, the M3A1 Scout Car was one of the first types of armoured vehicle to be supplied in 1941 by the United States to the United Kingdom. The American vehicles, although designated Scout Cars, did not correspond in size, manoeuvrability or performance to the British requirement for a scout car, although some appear temporarily to have been used as such by some units in the

United Kingdom awaiting supplies of Daimler Scout Cars. However, good use was made by the British Army of White Scout Cars, as they were usually called, as armoured personnel carriers (they carried eight men and were used chiefly in motor battalions of armoured divisions), as command vehicles and as armoured ambulances. Later the designation of Truck, 15 cwt., Personnel (White M3A1) was adopted by the War Office.

In American use, the armament usually consisted of a 0·5-in. M2 machine-gun (Browning) on a skate mounting travelling on a rail round the inside of the hull, and one or two 0·3-in. Browning machine-guns. These guns rarely seem to have been fitted in British-used vehicles in which, also, the front roller was often removed.

One illustration shows a Scout Car M3A1 of the U.S. Army; this has the canvas hood up. The other view is of a White Scout Car as used by the motor battalion (infantry) of a British armoured brigade in 1941.

39 Tanks, Light, Mark VIB and Mark VIC, U.K.

The culmination of a long series of Light Tanks stemming from the Carden-Loyd Mark VII, designed by Sir John Carden in 1928, the Light Tanks of the Mark VI series were numerically the most important armoured fighting vehicles of the British Army in 1939-40.

Designed, like its predecessors, by Vickers-Armstrongs Ltd., and also originally built by them, the Light Mark VI was one of the fighting vehicles chosen in 1935 for production by other manufactuers outside the armaments industry to familiarise them with this particular form of heavy engineering. The Mark VIB was a slightly improved version of the original Mark VI and was built in far greater quantity.

Following the pattern of its predecessors the Mark VI had the engine (an 88-h.p. six-cylinder Meadows) at the right-hand side of the hull with the transmission led forward to drive front sprockets. The driver sat at the left-hand side, and the turret, containing the commander and gunner, was also off-set to the left. The suspension consisted of two two-wheeled bogie units each side, sprung on twin coil springs, the rear road wheel acting also as a trailing idler. This form of Horstmann suspension was simple and dependable and although there was a tendency for the tracks to be shed, they could be replaced fairly easily.

The armament of the Mark VIB consisted of a Vickers 0·303-in. water-cooled machine-gun and a Vickers 0·5-in. heavy machine-gun. The Mark VIC, which followed the Mark VIB in production, was similar in almost all respects except that it lacked the turret cupola and had Besa machine-guns of 7·92 mm. and 15 mm. instead of the Vickers. In both models the maximum armour thickness was only 14 mm. and these tanks could be regarded as no more than reconnaissance vehicles. Nevertheless, Mark VIBs were employed in all the Divisional Cavalry Regiments of the British Expeditionary Force, and as headquarters tanks in the 1st Army Tank Brigade. Even in the 1st Armoured Division Light Mark VICs formed a high proportion of the tank strength because of the delay in delivery of Cruiser tanks and they were no match for most types of German tanks encountered in 1940. Mark VIBs and earlier light tanks were also employed in the earlier North African campaigns.

The illustrations show a Tank, Light Mark VIB of the 4th/7th Royal Dragoon Guards (the Divisional Cavalry Regiment of the 2nd Infantry Division, B.E.F.) and a Mark VIC of the 10th Royal Hussars, one of the tank regiments of the 2nd Armoured Brigade, 1st Armoured Division.

40 Tank, Infantry, Mark I, U.K.

Designed and built to the General Staff specification A.11 for a two-man infantry-accompanying tank, armoured against all known anti-tank guns and equipped with one machine-gun, the Infantry Mark I met all these requirements adequately. It also was relatively cheap to manufacture, another important consideration at the time.

Sir John Carden of Vickers-Armstrongs Ltd. undertook the design, and the prototype vehicle was ready by the Autumn of 1936. A small tank, the A.11 weighed 11 tons due to its heavy armour, on a 60-mm. basis. However, as only a low speed (8 m.p.h.) was required in a tank tied closely to the infantry advance it was possible to use the readily available and inexpensive Ford V-8 lorry engine and transmission. This was sited at the rear and drove rear sprockets, much of the final drive and steering systems being closely derived from other Vickers tracked vehicles. The suspension—two four-wheeled bogie units each side, sprung on semi-elliptic springs—was similar to that of the commercial Vickers 6-ton tank and Dragon Mark IV artillery tractor.

The armament of one Vickers 0·303-in. water-cooled machine-gun, mounted in the cast turret, was intended only for use against 'soft' targets, although the need for some means of attacking other armoured vehicles was subsequently recognised by substituting the Vickers 0·5-in. heavy machine-gun in some troop leaders' tanks.

An initial order placed in 1937 with Vickers-Armstrongs for sixty Infantry Mark Is was followed by another in 1938 for a further sixty and a final order in January 1939 for nineteen. These tanks were used to equip the 1st Army Tank Brigade which joined the British Expeditionary Force in France. In action, the Infantry Mark I's served their purpose quite well, within their known limitations—their armour proving to be highly effective.

The illustrations both show tanks of the 4th Battalion Royal Tank Regiment, which used an eye as its unit sign. One picture is of a tank in the 1939 plain green and the other shows a company commander's tank in France: this is one of the later production vehicles with minor changes, including the positioning of the headlamps.

41 Carro Armato M.11/39, Italy.

The principal Italian medium tank at the beginning of the Second World War, the first prototype of the Carro Armato M.11/39 was built in 1937. This tank had a suspension system scaled up from that of the L.3/35 although most of the other features of the layout of the subsequent production version were present. These were a rear-mounted engine with drive sprockets at the front; a 37-mm. gun in the front right-hand side of the hull, with the driver at the left side; and a machine-gun turret on the hull roof.

The suspension of the production model of the M.11/39 consisted of two four-wheel bogie units each side. Each group of four wheels was in two pairs, controlled by a single semi-elliptic leaf spring.

An excellent diesel engine powered this medium tank. It was an eight-cylinder model of V-form, the Spa 8T, which was rated at 105 h.p. and produced a maximum speed of 20 m.p.h.

The hull gun was a 37-mm. semi-automatic weapon based on an old Vickers design: it had only limited traverse. The turret armament was two 8-mm. Breda machine-guns in a twin mounting. Protection was at a maximum of 30 mm.

Although mechanically reliable, the M.11/39 was a poor fighting machine, with an ineffectual main armament. It was used in the campaigns in North and East Africa until about 1941, being replaced as soon as possible by the very much better M.13/40.

The illustrations show a tank in desert yellow with tactical markings representing the second tank of the second platoon of No. 2 Company of an Italian tank battalion.

42 Mittlerer Schützenpanzerwagen SdKfz 251, Germany.

Germany produced both armoured and unarmoured experimental half-track vehicles in the First World War. During the rearmament phase from 1933 onwards, however, development of this type of vehicle was, at first, concentrated on the unarmoured variety for which there was a great demand for use as artillery tractors and for other purposes.

One of the advantages of a half-track is that it is possible to have a long chassis that, in a fully tracked vehicle, might be difficult to steer. At the same time, a better general performance can usually be obtained than is possible in a full-tracked vehicle of similar dimensions. It is also usually possible to use a larger quantity of standard commercial components in a half-track than could be employed in a fully tracked vehicle.

By 1938 a wide range of half-tracked vehicles had been developed as artillery tractors, including the Borgward 3-ton model HL K1.6 for towing the 10·5-cm. light field howitzer. This chassis was selected for use as a basic armoured vehicle for infantry and other troops supporting the tanks in the Panzer Divisions and Büssing-NAG were given instructions to design the armoured hull. The chassis itself needed only minor modifications, chiefly in order to reduce the height of the bonnet.

Apart from a few prototypes, all the main types of German half tracks of the Second World War had the same mechanical layout of a front engine (a six-cylinder Maybach of 100 h.p. in the case of the SdKfz 251) with transmission leading back to drive sprockets at the front of the track assembly. The front wheels were not driven and were used to support the front of the vehicle and for steering. In a gradual turn, steering was achieved by means of the front wheels only, but further application of the steering wheel automatically brought steering brakes in the track system into operation.

The whole track assembly of the German half-tracks was complicated, expensive to produce and required a lot of maintenance, although it contributed largely to the high-speed performance of the vehicle. The suspension consisted of interleaved road wheels independently sprung on transverse torsion bars. The track, which was unique to this type of German vehicle, was made up of light weight cast links bearing rubber pads on the shoes. The links were joined by needle bearings which required individual lubrication.

The open-top armoured hull in the early versions (Ausf. A and B) of SdKfz 251 (shown in the illustrations) was assembled by means of a combination of bolting and welding. Later models were all-welded and the design (notably of the front nose plate) was progressively simplified to reduce production difficulties.

A few 3-ton armoured personnel carriers (gepanzerter Mannschafts Transportwagen) were issued to the Army in time for the Campaign in Poland and by May 1940 they were in wide use for the Campaign in the West. Production continued throughout the War, during which some 16,000 in twenty-two different versions were built. Of these, the SdKfz 251/3 Funkwagen (Wireless vehicle) (shown in one illustration) was widely used by unit and formation commanders, while the standard Schützenpanzerwagen SdKfz 251/1 used by Panzergrenadiers and for a variety of other units in armoured formations was numerically the most important variant.

43 Kleiner Panzerbefehlswagen I, Germany.

The need for commanders of tank units—at least up to Battalion and Regimental level—to maintain close contact with their tanks was well understood by the leaders of the German Army armoured forces, following experience gained in exercises. Gun tanks (Pzkpfw I) were at first modified as command vehicles until a more specialised command tank was developed.

The kleiner Panzerbefehlswagen ('small armoured command vehicle') was based on the chassis and running gear of the Pzkpfw I, Ausf. B. The turret was eliminated and the crew compartment was raised in height, thus providing somewhat cramped accommodation for a crew of three, two wireless sets and a map table. An observation cupola for the commander was provided in the hull roof. The only change to the automotive specification was an increase in the capacity of the dynamo, which was required in this version to keep the wireless batteries fully charged.

One machine-gun was provided in a ball mounting in the front plate of the hull. The armour protection of the PzBefswg. was considerably increased over that of the normal gun tank version, by 17 mm. on the front plate of the crew compartment and 10 mm. on the nose plate.

The two wireless sets (models FU.2 and FU.6) enabled the unit commander on the spot to maintain contact with both sub-units and higher formation headquarters, so that effective control over the battle could be exercised. This was an important factor in the Polish Campaign when these tanks were first used. At the opening of the 1940 Campaign in the West on 10 May, ninety-six klPzBefswg. were employed—about half of the total of 200 command vehicles on PzKpfw I chassis to be built. Thirty-nine command tanks on PzKpfw II were also used at this time.

44 Panzerkampfwagen III Ausf. E and G, Germany.

A 15-ton tank armed with a 3·7-cm. or 5-cm. armour-piercing weapon was planned as the basic equipment of the Panzer Divisions. This light tank was to be supplemented by a medium tank armed with a 7·5-cm. gun: the earlier light tanks Panzer I and II armed with nothing heavier than machine-guns or a 2-cm. gun were regarded as no more than stop-gaps.

Prototypes of the 'Zugführerwagen' ('platoon commanders vehicle'—abbreviated as ZW)—the code name for the 15-ton tank—were ordered from Daimler-Benz, Rheinmetall, MAN and Krupp. These prototype vehicles were tested in 1936–7 and, as a result, the Daimler-Benz model was chosen as the basis for further development. The early models (Ausf.A, B, C and D) had varying forms of suspension (although the hull and turret were more or less standardised) ranging from five largish road wheels on coil springs per side, in the Ausf.A, to eight small wheels on leaf springs in the Ausf.B, C and D.

About eighty of these early models were made but it was not until the advent of the Ausf.E that the suspension took the familiar form that was to be continued through the rest of the production life of the PzKpfw III. This consisted of six road wheels each side on a transverse torsion-bar suspension system. The upper run of the track was carried on three rollers per side.

In the Ausf.E a more powerful Maybach twelve-cylinder engine (model HL 120 TR) was fitted—this had an output of 300 h.p., compared with the 230–250 h.p. of the earlier models. The engine was mounted at the rear of the hull and transmitted power through a hydraulic clutch and a Maybach Variorex ten-speed gearbox to the driving sprockets at the front.

The turret of the Panzer III was situated approximately in the centre of the hull and mounted the main armament of a 3·7-cm. gun. General Guderian had wanted a 5-cm. gun for the Panzer III but in order to get production under way without controversy the smaller gun of the same calibre as the standard infantry anti-tank gun was accepted. It was not, in fact, until after the French campaign that the 5-cm. gun began to be fitted to Panzer IIIs. Coaxial armament was one machine-gun (MG 34) and another was mounted in the front of the hull beside the driver.

A few PzKpfw IIIs, mainly the earliest models, but including some Ausf.Es, were used in the Polish Campaign. In May 1940, at the beginning of the campaign in the West, 349 Panzer IIIs were employed and formed the core of the attack.

Some 3,200 tanks were available at the beginning of the campaign in Russia in June 1941 and a high proportion of these was Panzer IIIs. By this time a 5-cm. gun had been introduced into the PzKpfw III by progressive replacement of the 3·7-cm. weapon in existing vehicles and as the standard equipment in new tanks produced from the latter part of 1940 onwards.

The pictures show a PzKpfw III, Ausf.E, as it appeared (with the unusual tactical number 200) in the Western Campaign and a PzKpfw III, Ausf.G, armed with a 5-cm. KwK.L/42, of the 3rd Panzer Division in Russia.

45 **Panzerkampfwagen IV, Ausf.A and B,** Germany.

The fourth and, as it proved, the most enduring of the main types of tank with which Germany rearmed and entered the Second World War was the Panzer IV.

This was specified as a medium tank in the 20-ton class, to be armed with a 7·5-cm. gun, capable of giving fire support to the lighter tanks armed only with armour-piercing weapons or machine-guns. The code name adopted for this type was Bataillonsführerwagen (BW for short)—'battalion commander's vehicle'.

Designs in varying forms to meet this specification were submitted by Rheinmetall-Borsig, MAN and Krupp. Some of these designs did not get off paper, but following tests with prototype vehicles in 1935–6 Krupp were awarded the order for development of the production model.

Krupp's earlier proposals for the suspension of the BW were for interleaved road wheels of the kind that were eventually to be adopted in later tanks, but the form of suspension actually used throughout the long production run of the BW, or Panzerkampfwagen IV, as it became designated, was much more simple. The eight road wheels each side were suspended in pairs on leaf springs; the idler wheel was off the ground at the rear and the top run of the track was carried on four return rollers—an easy-to-remember recognition point for the Panzer IV. As with the other main German tanks of the period, the engine was situated at the rear with the transmission led forward to final drive via sprockets at the front of the track.

The engine was the same as that used in the Panzer III (from Ausf.E onwards)—the twelve-cylinder Maybach HL 108TR. The arrangement differed from the smaller tank in that the cooling air was drawn in at the right-hand side of the hull and after passing through the radiator was expelled through grilles at the left-hand side. The power was transmitted to the drive sprockets through a dry plate clutch and gearbox which, in the Ausf.A, had five forward speeds. This was increased to six in Ausf.B and subsequent models in which also the engine was the larger Maybach HL 120 TR (HL 120 TRM from Ausf.C onwards). These mechanical changes constituted the principal differences between the first two production models of this tank. The Pzkpfw IV Ausf.A and B are shown in the pictures, but all the earlier models of the Panzer IV were very much alike externally and all (until the introduction in early 1942, in the later vehicles of Ausf.F, of the long 7·5-cm. KwK L/43) had the short-barrelled 7·5-cm. KwK L/24 as main armament. There was a coaxial machine-gun in all tanks of the series and all except Ausf.B and C also had another MG.34 in the front of the hull to the right of the driver.

The armour basis of the hull of the PzKpfw IV Ausf.A was 14·5 mm. and of the turret 20 mm. The frontal armour in the next three models, Ausf.B–D, was increased to 30 mm. Some 270 of these early models of Panzer IV were built between 1936 and 1939 and the opportunity was taken to try them out in the Polish Campaign. As a result it was decided to increase the armour thickness at the front of the hull to 60 mm. and at the sides to 40 mm., and the new model was known as Ausf.D. The design was otherwise unchanged except in minor details and 278 Panzer IVs of all models were available at the beginning of the campaign in the West in 1940. Production was stepped up in 1940 and the next year so that over 1,000 had been built by the end of 1941. In Russia, with its original armament, the Panzer IV was found to be capable of tackling the Russian T.34 only from the rear, so an emergency programme of up-gunning had to be undertaken. As a result the Panzer IV remained a useful tank even to the end of the war—a tribute to the quality of its original design.

46 15-cm. s.I.G. on Panzerkampfwagen I, Ausf.B, Germany.

The PzKpfw I, Ausf.B, chassis was used to give greater mobility to the German 15-cm. heavy infantry gun in a conversion carried out by Alkett at Berlin-

Spandau. Some of these were first employed in action in Poland and others saw service later, in the Western campaign. Thirty-eight conversions were completed and this was the first German self-propelled gun of its kind. Many similar improvisations, in which a gun on a more or less standard field-mounting with a light armoured shield was fitted on to a tank chassis with only slight modifications, were to follow later in the Second World War.

47 Panzerjäger I, Germany

This was the first German 'tank hunter' self-propelled anti-tank gun and consisted of a Czech 4·7-cm. anti-tank gun in a limited traverse field mounting on a Pzkpfw I, Ausf.B chassis.

About 170 tank chassis were converted in this way by Alkett of Berlin-Spandau between 1939 and 1941. The conversion was a relatively simple one and involved little more than removal of the turret and substitution of the 4·7-cm. Czech anti-tank gun with a three-sided shield, open at the rear. Stowage for eighty-six rounds was provided.

Vehicles of this kind were employed in infantry anti-tank units with the Afrika Korps in 1941 and in the opening stages of the Russian Campaign.

48 Pantserwagen M'39 (DAF), Holland.

The six-wheeled Van Doorne armoured car was designed in eight months in answer to a suggestion that the DAF factory should produce under licence a British design of armoured car for the Dutch Army.

The DAF armoured car proved to be a very advanced concept for its time and consequently some were ordered for the Dutch Army and twelve were built by 15 May 1940, after which the factory was taken over by the Germans.

Both well armed and armoured, the DAF was equipped with a turret mounting a 37-mm. Bofors gun and a 7·9-mm. machine-gun, and there were two further machine-guns in the front and the rear of the hull. The hull armour was exceptionally well designed, with sloping glacis plates at front and rear as well as angled side plates.

A Ford (Mercury) V-8 engine of 95 h.p. was located at the rear of the hull at the right-hand side with a transfer box alongside to take the transmission to a Trado rear axle through which the power was transmitted to all four rear wheels. The rear machine-gunner, who sat beside the engine, was provided with a second set of driving controls for driving the car backwards in an emergency.

The twelve DAF armoured cars, not all of which were fully equipped or provided with their armament when the Germans invaded Holland, took no part in the fighting. They were subsequently used by the Germans for internal security duties.

49 Tank, Cruiser, Mark I, U.K.

Designed originally as a potential replacement for the old Medium Tanks, Marks I and II, used by the Royal Tank Corps, this tank, known originally as A.9 from its General Staff specification number, became the first of the new class of Cruiser Tanks called for under the new official policy formulated in 1936.

Sir John Carden, working for Vickers-Armstrongs, designed the A.9, which followed the broad layout of the Medium Mark III (which had not been produced in numbers because of its high cost at the time) but was lighter and was intended to use a commercially available engine. An A.E.C. six-cylinder 150-h.p. engine similar to that used in buses was eventually settled on for the power unit: this was a diesel engine converted for use with petrol. The gearbox was a Meadows five-speed model.

The main armament was planned as a 3-pr (47-mm.)—the standard gun in British tanks—but this was replaced in production models by the new 2-pr (40-mm.), which was smaller but had a higher muzzle velocity. The main turret incorporated power traverse—an innovation in British tanks at this time. In addition to the coaxial Vickers 0·303-in. machine-gun, two further Vickers guns were carried in two small auxiliary turrets—one either side of the driver's cab. A proportion of Cruiser Mark Is were fitted with a 3·7-in. howitzer instead of the 2-pr to act as close support vehicles able to put down high-explosive fire and lay smoke.

Following trials, during which some unreliable features in the pilot model, including a track-shedding propensity, were dealt with, a production order for fifty tanks was given to Vickers-Armstrongs in August 1937, together with an order for seventy-five to Harland and Wolff, of Belfast. Deliveries of completed tanks began late in 1939 and ran through until about the spring of 1940, although the supplies of weapons did not always keep pace with the production of the vehicles.

Cruiser Mark Is were used in action by the 1st Armoured Division in France in 1940 and one of the illustrations shows a close support tank of Headquarters, 'A' Squadron, 3rd Royal Tank Regiment, of this Division. They were also employed with the 2nd and 7th Armoured Division in the earlier North African campaigns and the other illustration is of a tank belonging to 1st Royal Tank Regiment of the latter formation.

50   **Tank, Cruiser, Mark IIA, U.K.**

The General Staff specification A.10 was for an infantry-accompanying tank. The design for this tank, produced by Sir John Carden for Vickers-Armstrongs, was based very closely on that of A.9. The mechanical components of transmission and suspension were almost identical, although lower gear ratios had to be used to deal with the extra weight brought about by an increase of the armour maximum of 14 mm. on A.9 to 30 mm. (as finally specified) for A.10.

The hull design of the A.10 was simpler than that of A.9 in that the two auxiliary turrets (cramped, and highly unpopular with tank crews) were eliminated, a single machine-gun in the right-hand side of the hull, beside the driver, taking their place.

The extra armour thickness on the A.9 was achieved by bolting additional plates on to the hull and the turret. By the time the A.9 was ready for production, in early 1938, the armour maximum of 30 mm. was considered inadequate for an infantry tank (the specification for A.11 already called for 60 mm.) but it was, nevertheless, decided to produce the A.10, although as a 'heavy cruiser' tank. Limited orders were placed with Vickers-Armstrongs, Metropolitan-Cammell Carriage & Wagon Co., and Birmingham Railway Carriage & Wagon Co. for an eventual total of 160 vehicles. Most of these were completed during 1940, the last in the late autumn. Early in the course of production, the Besa 7·92-mm. machine-gun was introduced in place of the Vickers and the tanks with this weapon were designated Cruiser, Mark IIA. The bulk of the A.10s built were, in fact, in this form. A proportion of all A.10s were, at the same time, fitted out as close support tanks in which the 2-pr main armament was replaced by a 3·7-in. howitzer.

The distribution of the Cruiser Mark II and IIA paralleled that of the Cruiser Mark I and they were used in France in 1940 and in the Desert Campaigns until about the end of 1941. In service, the A.10 proved rather more popular with its crews than the A.9 since, although slower, it was more reliable, better protected and lacked the disliked auxiliary turrets.

One illustration shows a Cruiser Mark IIA with which the 5th Royal Tank Regiment (1st Armoured Division) was re-equipped in the United Kingdom after the withdrawal from France in 1940. This tank has no machine-guns, which were then in short supply. The other view shows a tank of the 2nd Armoured Division as it appeared in North Africa early in 1941. The addition of sand shields over the tracks and a water drum will be noticed.

51 Tanks, Cruiser, Marks IV and IVA, U.K.

The War Office was made aware in 1936 of the potential of the American Christie tank for development as a British medium or cruiser tank. This knowledge was gained at second hand, because although the Christie tank with its unique suspension had been around since 1928, it was not until Lt.-Col. (later General) G. le Q. Martel saw a demonstration of the Russian-built version that the merits of the design were given serious consideration.

With remarkable promptitude a Christie tank was purchased for the War Office (through the medium of Morris Cars Ltd., part of the Nuffield organisation) and this arrived in England in November 1936.

This tank was tested and it was decided to adopt two salient features of the design—a powerful Liberty modified aero engine and the high-speed suspension system—for a British cruiser tank. The alternative of running on wheels, another Christie feature, was rightly decided by the War Office as being an unnecessary complication and it is worthy of note that the Russians also took this viewpoint in their later developments of the Christie design.

A specification, A.13, was drawn up and Morris Commercial Cars Ltd., (another company of the Nuffield group) were asked to build two prototypes. After trials of these and the inclusion of modifications one of which was, on Lord Nuffield's personal instructions, the substitution of shorter-pitched tracks, a first production order for what was to be designated Tank,

Cruiser, Mark III, was awarded to Nuffield Mechanisations & Aero Ltd. This contract, for sixty-five tanks, was dated 22 January 1938, and the first vehicles were delivered to the Army in early 1939. Ease of mass-production had been given some thought in the design, probably for the first time in a British tank. By this time it was decided that the original 14-mm. armour maximum was insufficient and 30 mm. was required.

The increased armour was achieved by a redesign, known ultimately as Cruiser, Mark IV, in which extra plates were added to hull and turret frontal surfaces and spaced plates (of diamond form in front view) were added to the turret sides. Some Mark IIIs were subsequently reworked, wholly or partially, to the Mark IV standard.

The armament on all A.13 cruiser tanks consisted of a 2-pr gun with a coaxial machine-gun in the turret. On the later Mark IVs to be produced, however, the original Vickers 0·303-in. machine-gun was replaced by a Besa 7·92-mm. and these vehicles were designated Mark IVA. A few tanks were fitted for close support with 3-in. howitzers instead of 2-prs but many regiments re-equipped with Cruiser Mark IVs still retained earlier cruiser tanks for this function.

The engine of the Cruiser Tanks Marks III and IV was a Nuffield-built Liberty V-12 cylinder of 340 h.p. which transmitted its power via a multiplate clutch and a four-speed gearbox to rear sprockets. Steering was of the clutch and brake type. The suspension, which, with the high power/weight ratio, was mainly responsible for the A.13's good performance (30 m.p.h. maximum, reduced from the prototype's 45 m.p.h.), consisted of four large road wheels each side. These were mounted on trailing or leading pivot arms, controlled by long coil springs, contained between inner and outer walls of the hull sides.

Three hundred and thirty-five Tanks, Cruiser, Marks III, IV and IVA, were built. Some of all Marks were sent to France with the 1st Armoured Division in 1940 and others (Mark IVA) were used in action in the North African campaigns, where their speed was a great asset, until late 1941. One illustration shows a tank of the Queen's Bays of the 1st Armoured Division in France (this is a Mark IV or a Mark III converted to the same standard) and the other is of a Cruiser Mark IVA (with the earlier, rectangular type of gun mantlet) of the 5th Royal Tank Regiment as it appeared in North Africa.

52 Tank, Infantry, Mark II, Matilda, U.K.

It can be claimed that the Infantry Mark II was one of the best British tanks of the Second World War, because at the time of its appearance on the battle scene it was at least as well armed as the majority of its German opponents and much better armoured. The counterattack by the 1st Army Tank Brigade near Arras on 21 May 1940 was the only real tactical shock received by the Germans in the invasion of France, and even Rommel (then commanding the 7th Panzer Division) described the situation at one stage as 'an extremely tight spot'. In the early Western Desert campaigns, the Matilda was superior to all Italian tanks and ruled the battlefield.

The weakness of an infantry tank without the capability of tackling enemy armoured vehicles was realised even during the development of the Infantry Mark I, and accordingly the new specification A.12 was drawn up for a heavier tank equipped with a 2-pr gun to succeed the earlier design. Taking the experimental Medium Tank A.7 (three prototypes were built between 1929 and 1937) as a basis, the Director of Tank Design drew up for the Mechanisation Board the essential design features of the A.12, Infantry Mark II. A contract for development, followed by eventual production, was then awarded to the Vulcan Foundry Ltd.

The essentials of the Infantry Mark II (later known as Matilda) were a 2-pr gun and coaxial machine-gun in the turret, armour increased to a maximum of 78 mm., a four-man crew and a top speed nearly double that of its predecessor. The general layout was the same as that of the later Vickers Medium tanks A.6 and A.7 and the suspension—two-wheeled bogie units on coil springs—was of the kind originally used in the commercial Vickers Mark C sold to Japan. To provide the necessary power and, at the same time, to ease production problems, two standard A.E.C. diesel engines (each six-cylinder, 87-h.p.) were used in Matilda I and Matilda II, although these were replaced by Leyland diesels (total 190 h.p.) in Matilda III and subsequent models. The machine-gun coaxial with the 2-pr gun in Matilda I, the first model of Infantry Mark II, was a water-cooled Vickers 0·303-in. This was the

model used with the B.E.F. in France—all were at first issued to the 7th Battalion Royal Tank Regiment although later a few were transferred to the 4th Battalion to give fire support to that unit's Infantry Mark Is. Matilda II and subsequent models used in later actions all had a Besa machine-gun replacing the Vickers.

A feature found only in the early Matildas was a higher form of suspension than that used in later production models, where the armoured skirting gave more protection to the road wheels. This early suspension is shown in both illustrations, which are of tanks of the 7th Battalion Royal Tank Regiment. Also shown in one view is the trench-crossing tail device that was designed and built hurriedly to meet a demand in March 1940 from the troops in France.

53 Tanks, Light (Wheeled) Marks I and IA, U.K.

Following a series of eliminating tests in 1938, a modified Guy Quad-Ant chassis was chosen for production as the first British-built, four-wheeled, four-wheel drive, armoured car for the British Army. The normal version of the Quad-Ant was an artillery tractor with the engine in front, but for the armoured car the engine was placed at the rear, at the time a layout unusual in British armoured cars. The hull and turret were designed at Woolwich Arsenal with armour on a 15-mm. basis and armament consisting of a 0·303-in. Vickers machine-gun and a 0·5-in. Vickers heavy machine-gun mounted coaxially in the turret. This specification corresponded closely to that of the current Light Tank, Mark VIB, and the new official nomenclature of Tank, Light (Wheeled) Mark I, was adopted for the armoured car.

A contract for the production of 101 vehicles was awarded to Guy Motors Ltd. in January 1939. The prototype vehicles followed the then usual riveted form of construction for their hulls and turrets and this was originally specified in the production contract. However, Guy Motors asked and obtained permission to employ instead welding for the construction of hulls and turrets, and a successful technique for carrying this out was devised by the Company. When in 1940 a much larger output of all types of military vehicles was required, Guy Motors handed over the designs and production technique to the Rootes Group, by whom they were used for the Humber Armoured Cars. The last fifty-one Guy Armoured Cars to be built under the contract had the armament changed to a 7·92-mm. and a 15-mm. Besa machine-gun. The first Humber armoured cars had this armament and were almost identical in external appearance to the Guys.

The Guy Armoured Car had a 53-h.p. Meadows engine from which the transmission was taken via a transfer box to differentials on the front and rear axles. Somewhat underpowered, the maximum speed was about 40 m.p.h.

'No. 3 Air Mission' (a special G.H.Q. liaison unit with the British Expeditionary Force) included what was known as a Phantom Squadron comprised of six Guy Armoured Cars —the only ones to be used in France. Following the evacuation of the B.E.F.,

a troop of Guy Armoured Cars from July 1940 to March 1941 provided the protection for the detachment operating Humber Ironside Special Saloons and other cars for the transport of Royalty and Cabinet Ministers. Guy Armoured Cars were also used for defence (and later for training) in the United Kingdom and the illustrations show them in this role. The Guy Mark I is as it appeared in July 1940 with the 2nd Northamptonshire Yeomanry, of the Yeomanry Armoured Detachment —a formation later equipped with tanks as the 20th Armoured Brigade. The Mark IA bears the unit code sign (47) of an armoured car regiment in the United Kingdom in 1941.

54 Car, Scout, Mark I, U.K.

The Daimler Scout Car was one of the most effective items of equipment of its kind to be built and was widely used in the British Army for scouting and liaison purposes.

The original specification drawn up by the War Office early in 1938 called for a small vehicle with frontal armour of at least 25 mm. capable of resisting infantry light anti-tank weapons and able to head a column of tanks or other vehicles likely to encounter opposition. A 0·303-in. Bren light machine-gun was to be carried and the vehicle was to be able to withdraw quickly in reverse. For this reason only frontal armour was specified: for the sake of lightness no other armour was called for.

Three designs were submitted and tested in the latter half of 1938 and eventually the one from B.S.A. Cycles Ltd. was selected. During the development of this vehicle, light side armour was at first added, as much as a means of supporting the heavy 30-mm. glacis plate as for crew protection. Then, the War Office decided that the side armour must be to a 14-mm. standard, an armoured roof must be added and the bonnet of the engine (at the rear) must also be protected. The modified vehicle was ready by January 1939 and about six months later a preliminary order for fifty-two cars (later increased to 172) was given to the Daimler Co. Ltd. who, in the meantime, had taken over the project from B.S.A.

The B.S.A./Daimler (later known simply as 'Daimler') Scout Car was powered by a six-cylinder 55-h.p. engine mounted at the rear. The drive was taken forward through a 'Fluid Flywheel' and pre-selector gearbox to a transfer box in the centre of the vehicle. This box had a single differential, from one half of which propellor shafts, universally jointed, led forward to a front wheel and back to the rear wheel on the same side. Similar shafts led from the other half of the differential to the wheels on the other side of the vehicle. At each wheel station 'Tracta' joints were used. This system left more space in the centre of the hull than a more conventional transmission and enabled the overall height of the vehicle to be reduced. The suspension was independent, using coil springs at each wheel. Steering was on all four wheels, which made for a small turning circle and, incidentally, gave considerable difficulties for drivers lacking experience. A high speed in reverse could be obtained in the Scout Car and this was facilitated for the driver by the position of his seat, which was turned inwards slightly, enabling

him more readily to look over his left shoulder.

The crew compartment, in which the Bren gunner sat beside the driver, was octagonal-shaped in plan, with the upper half of the side sloping inwards, and the lower half undercut. A sliding armoured roof was fitted.

Scout Cars, Mark I, were used in action in France in 1940 with two experimental platoons of the 4th Battalion Royal Northumberland Fusiliers, an infantry division reconnaissance unit, otherwise chiefly equipped with motor-cycles. A car of this unit, with its white and red pennant, is shown in one of the illustrations. They were also used in formation, regimental and squadron headquarters in the 1st Armoured Division in France in 1940 and subsequently, together with later Marks, with most other British Armoured formations. The second illustration is of a Scout Car with the 2nd Armoured Division in Libya.

A total of 6,626 Daimler Scout Cars of all Marks was eventually built; even so, the demand always exceeded the supply.

55 KV I(B) (Heavy Tank), U.S.S.R.

The KV heavy tank (the initials stand for Klementy Voroshilov, a Marshal of the Soviet Union) was the third of a trio of designs in 1938 for a modern type to take the place of the old and unsatisfactory T-35.

The first two models (T-100 and SMK) both had two turrets (reduced at the drawing-board stage from three, at the suggestion of Stalin) and the other, which later was evolved as the KV I, had only one turret. It was, again, Stalin's influence that led to the choice of this model.

The KV I was designed as a heavy tank to enjoy the maximum protection from contemporary armour-piercing weapons coupled with an effective armament, in which the total weight should not become excessive and so cut down on mobility. A prototype of this tank was completed in September 1939 and several pre-production vehicles were in use on the Finnish front before the end of the year. This helped in the perfection of several features, including the torsion-bar suspension system, a type which was taken over from the T-100 but modified for the KV I.

The main features of the layout of the KV I were a centrally mounted turret containing a 76·2-mm. gun and two machine-guns (one coaxial, one in the rear face); the driver's compartment at the front with a hull machine-gun position to the left of the driver, and a rear-mounted diesel engine. This was a V-form twelve-cylinder power unit of 550 h.p. which drove rear sprockets via a five-speed gearbox. The tracks were exceptionally wide—27½ in.— and this helped to keep ground pressure down to little more than that of the very much lighter BT-7. Armour protection was on a generous basis, to around 100 mm. on the front of the hull and turret.

During the course of production of the KV series, improvements in both armour and armament were introduced, some tanks having a longer calibre 76·2-mm. gun and others, like the KV IB (shown in the illustrations), with both hull and turret armour supplemented by the addition of extra plates. In the case of the KV IB (the suffix was added by the Germans, incidentally, as a means of identifying this model) the additional plates were welded on to the glacis and driver's plates but bolted on to the hull and turret sides. The bolt heads were a particularly prominent feature on the turret.

Although inevitably outmoded as the War progressed, the KV I proved to be a very good design which was later used for the basis of the Stalin tank.

56 KV II (Heavy Tank), U.S.S.R.

First appearing in early 1940, this massive and cumbersome vehicle was an 'artillery tank' version of the KV I. A 152-mm. howitzer (122-mm. calibre in the very earliest models) mounted in a high, square turret took the place of the normal 76·2-mm. gun turret. This turret had a 360-degree traverse but it weighed around 12 tons and the bearings were badly designed, so that it could only be traversed when the tank was on level ground. The increase in all-up weight of about 10 tons without any increase in power, coupled with much higher centre of gravity, inevitably decreased mobility, although in any case the gun could not be fired on the move.

KV IIs used the same chassis as KV Is and the later versions of the former (known as KV IIB by the Germans) had the wider tracks of the KV IB as well as a slightly different turret and gun mounting.

The KV IIs had some success when employed in the assault on the Mannerheim Line in Finland but were found to be virtually useless when meeting the German invasion of Russia in the Summer of 1941 and they do not appear to have been used after 1941. Since the chassis were identical with those of the KV I, however, it seems likely that most KV IIs which survived were converted to KV Is.

57 South African Reconnaissance Car, Mark II, South Africa.

South African-built armoured cars made a valuable contribution to the British Commonwealth war effort, particularly in the campaign in East Africa in 1940 and in the North African battles in 1941–2, when armoured cars from the United Kingdom were in short supply.

When the Second World War broke out in September 1939, it was discovered by the South Africans that little help with supplies of armoured cars or even suitable designs was available from the United Kingdom. Accordingly, work on an armoured car based on the Ford 3-ton lorry chassis, which was already in progress, was joined by further design work for a similar armoured car on a similar Ford chassis but with the Marmon-Herrington conversion to four-wheel drive. The new prototype was ready by 18 September and after extensive tests over the next few months, which brought out the need for improvements in the engine cooling and suspension, the 4 × 4 car was put into production. Orders were increased in mid-1940 when the Germans invaded France and Italy entered the war, to reach a total of 1,000 of these first two types of South African Reconnaissance Car, as

they were designated—Mark I, the original 4 × 2 type of which only 113 were built, and Mark II, the four-wheel drive version.

Armoured cars of both types were first used in action against the Italians in East Africa in 1940. The first supplies (of Mark IIs) for the Middle East for use in the North African campaigns were received about March 1941. These cars, when supplied to orders from the British War Office, were designated 'Armoured Car, Marmon-Herrington, Mark II'.

In their original form the South African Reconnaissance Cars consisted of an armoured hull, either riveted on to a mild steel frame, or welded, and mounted on the lorry chassis, which was shortened to a 134-in. wheelbase and strengthened. The welded type of hull soon predominated and replaced the riveted kind. The original armament consisted of a 0·303-in. Vickers machine-gun in a ball mounting in the turret and another Vickers in the left-hand side of the hull. This last was of little practical use and an alternative anti-aircraft mounting was provided. Cars in this form were used by the Union Defence Forces in East Africa, but many of those sent to the Middle East (where they were widely used by British and South African armoured car regiments) had a Bren 0·303-in. light machine-gun and a Boys 0·55-in. anti-tank rifle in the turret and an anti-aircraft machine-gun (Bren and/or Vickers). The hull mounting was often plated over.

Both illustrations show a South African Reconnaissance Car, Mark II, with welded hull and the original armament.

58 Leichter Panzerspähwagen SdKfz 222, Germany.

This light four-wheeled armoured car was the second model to be developed on the basis of the 'standard chassis I for heavy passenger cars'. This type of chassis (which, in spite of its designation, seems to have been used almost exclusively for armoured cars) was a rear-engined model with four-wheel drive and steering on all wheels.

The first type, SdKfz 221, was a two-man vehicle armed with a machine-gun only, but the second type, ordered in the Spring of 1940, had a hull slightly redesigned to give more room for the crew of three, and a larger turret equipped with a 2-cm. gun in addition to a machine-gun. The dual mount of these guns was intended to be fully available for anti-aircraft use and was a variant of the 2-cm. field mounting for which the turret was, in effect, a gun shield. The turret had no roof but to provide some protection against grenades was equipped with wire grilles, hinged at the sides.

The earlier light 4 × 4 armoured cars of the series had a 3,517-c.c. Horch V-8 engine but the SdKfz 222s used the Ausf.B chassis with the enlarged 3,823-c.c. engine and hydraulic instead of mechanical brakes. Weighing only about 4·7 tons, these armoured cars had a good performance and although production was ended in 1942, served well throughout the war from the French campaign onwards (the SdKfz 221 was used additionally in Poland). The performance was, to some extent, at the expense of armour, much of which was only on an 8-mm. basis. The frontal armour was to a maximum of 14·5 mm., but to supplement this a spaced shield was added experimentally in front of the nose plate of one car in the French campaign. This vehicle is shown in one of the illustrations, together with a standard SdKfz 222 in North African colours. The spaced shield was not adopted permanently for the light armoured cars although it was later a feature on some of the German eight-wheeled armoured cars.

59 Schützenpanzerwagen SdKfz 250 and 252, Germany.

More or less a scaled-down version of the 3-ton SdKfz 251, the 1-ton SdKfz 250 series appeared some two years after the heavier vehicle. Development of this light armoured half-track was entrusted to the firms of Demag AG, who provided the chassis, and Büssing-NAG, who designed the body.

The chassis used was a shortened version of the Demag D.7 (used as a light artillery tractor, etc.) in which one of the overlapping road wheels was eliminated each side. A Maybach six-cylinder 100-h.p. engine of similar type to that employed in the SdKfz 251 series was used, in conjunction with a seven-speed gearbox. The SdKfz 250 had a better performance (37 m.p.h. maximum speed) than the SdKfz 251 and tended to be issued more widely to reconnaissance units.

Using the same chassis as the SdKfz 250, but with an armoured hull developed separately by Wegmann, the SdKfz 252 was intended specifically as an ammunition carrier for Sturmgeschütz units. This vehicle had a fully enclosed hull with a long sloping rear plate, which helped to distinguish it from the various vehicles of the SdKfz 250 series. Also, the maximum armour thickness was slightly greater. The advantages of the special design of the SdKfz 252 were not great enough to justify an entirely different hull design, however, and the type was discontinued by 1941, when its function was taken over by versions of the SdKfz 250 series.

The SdKfz 252 did not normally carry mounted armament, but most of the vehicles of the SdKfz 250 series as armoured personnel carriers or wireless/command vehicles frequently had a light machine-gun MG.34 mounted at the forward end of the crew compartment. The crew of vehicles of this type varied between two for ammunition carriers to six for armoured personnel carriers.

The SdKfz 250 first appeared in action in the French campaign in 1940, although it is possible that the armoured ammunition carrier SdKfz 252 was issued slightly earlier to the troops. About 7,500 vehicles of the SdKfz 250/252 type were built during the War in fourteen different versions, two of which are shown in the illustrations: a standard Schützenpanzerwagen SdKfz 250/1 (as it appeared in Russia in 1941) and an armoured ammunition carrier (le. gep. Mun. Transportswagen, SdKfz 252).

60 **Sturmgeschütz III,** Germany.

An armoured self-propelled gun to support infantry in the attack was called for in 1936, and the firms of Daimler-Benz and Krupp were selected to undertake the development of the chassis and armament respectively.

The chassis of the Panzerkampfwagen III, then under development by Daimler-Benz was, not surprisingly, chosen for the basis of the new assault gun and the armament was the 7·5-cm. L/24. This gun was similar to that mounted in the PzKpfw IV tank but as a low silhouette was required in the assault gun and all round traverse was not considered essential it was possible to have this gun on the smaller chassis with much heavier armour (50-mm. front; 30-mm. sides and rear) at a not greatly excessive increase in weight.

The prototypes and early production models of Stu G III were based on the contemporary PzKpfw III chassis models—Ausf. E and F. Later production versions likewise used the later Panzer III chassis and so, throughout, the assault gun was mechanically the same as the tank.

The 7·5-cm. gun fitted low in the hull front plate had a traverse of $12\frac{1}{2}$ degrees either side, elevation of 20 degrees and depression of 10 degrees. The short barrelled version (L/24) of the gun was fitted throughout 1940–1 and it was only in 1942 that a longer weapon began to be used.

The Stu G III was first used in small numbers in the Western Campaign in 1940, although a total of 184 was produced by the end of the year and a further 548 in 1941. Over 10,500 Stu G III of various types were completed by the end of the War. This type of vehicle was first introduced into action by Germany and was a very successful weapon. Although later in the war production difficulties caused the Germans to use some Sturmgeschütz in place of tanks, when properly employed they were very effective.

The tank which had the greatest impact on the course of the Second World War was probably the Russian T-34. Although not the best in a mechanical sense, and the T-34 had several shortcomings in design, this Russian tank was nevertheless one of the most effective fighting vehicles of all time and its influence is still felt today.

Developed from the BT series through several intermediate experimental models, during which the ability to run on wheels was finally abandoned, the T-34 was designed in 1939 under a team headed by M. I. Koshkin, and the first prototypes were running early in 1940. Some modifications were made and the first production models came off the line at the Kirov Tank Plant in June 1940. As mass production got under way, increasing numbers of T-34s became available so that by the time of the German invasion of Russia in 1941, over 1,200 had been built.

The most remarkable feature of the T-34 when it first appeared was the extremely effective use of sloped armour plates for the hull. This fact, coupled with a good gun (the 76·2-mm. L/30·5 in the first production model) and a diesel engine of 500 h.p., which ensured good mobility, added up to make a tank which had a traumatic effect on the Wehrmacht. This even led to the impractical suggestion that the T-34 should be copied and made in Germany.

Few features of the T-34 were original, because most of them had appeared in one form or another in earlier Russian or foreign tanks, but it was the combination in one vehicle that was the great achievement of the designers. The general layout of the T-34 followed that of the BT series, with the engine at the rear driving rear track sprockets. The suspension was of the usual Christie type, with large road wheels on pivot arms controlled by long coil springs. The track design was unusual, though, in that the wide (19-in.) plates were held together by pins which were retained in place only by plates, attached to the hull, which pushed back the heads of any projecting pins as they passed. This system had obvious advantages in simplifying track manufacture and maintenance.

The twelve-cylinder V-form diesel engine of the T-34 was tried out in the BT-7M, the last of the BT series, and performed well in the T-34, although the transmission system at first gave trouble—faults probably of manufacture rather than design, though.

The hull of the T-34 in its early versions was 45 mm. thick at the front and 40 mm. at the sides and was divided internally by one bulkhead separating the engine from the crew compartment. The driver sat at the front with, beside him, the co-driver, who operated a machine-gun mounted in the glacis plate. The turret, mounted near the front of the hull roof, was protected mainly on a 45-mm. basis on early T-34s, and the 76·2-mm. gun shared a mounting with a 7·62-mm. machine-gun. The first 115 tanks built followed earlier practice in having an additional machine-gun in the turret rear face, but this was abandoned in later machines.

The gun mantlet in the first T-34

production model (this had no distinctive Russian nomenclature but was called T34/76A by the Germans, a practice adopted by the British) was of the external type, cast, and of a form (when used on the Sturmgeschutz III) known to the Germans as 'saukopf' (pig's head). This early T-34 (T 34/76A) is shown in the illustrations.

62 Autoblinda 40, Italy.

Some interesting mechanical features were included in this armoured car, the prototype of which, built by Spa, was completed by mid-1939. The most unusual point about the Autoblinda 40 was its transmission system. From the rear-mounted engine (a six-cylinder Spa of 80 h.p.) the drive was transmitted through a dry plate clutch to a five-speed and overdrive crash-type gearbox, built integrally with the clutch housing. All speeds except the fifth and overdrive sixth were also available in reverse. From the gearbox the drive was transmitted to a distribution box located approximately in the centre of the vehicle and incorporating a differential unit. The drive direct to each wheel was taken by helical bevel gear wheels through universally jointed shafts: a layout in plan which resembled a St. Andrew's cross.

The steering system operated on all four wheels and for emergency driving in reverse a second steering wheel, together with basic driving controls, was fitted. The suspension was of the independent coil spring type and the brakes hydraulic.

The hull of the AB 40 consisted of flat armour plates, varying between 8½-mm. and 6-mm., bolted or riveted

to a framework, the whole being bolted to the chassis frame. The turret (armoured to a maximum of 18 mm. and minimum of 6 mm.) was derived from an early design for the L.6/40 tank and mounted two 8-mm. Breda machine-guns. The fixed armament was completed by a further 8-mm. machine-gun mounted at the rear of the fighting compartment, at the right-hand side, to fire over the engine.

Two drivers, a commander/gunner and a rear gunner made up the crew of the AB 40. Weighing about 6½ tons and with a top speed of 46 m.p.h., the AB 40 was a suitable reconnaissance vehicle for employment in the North African desert and this was where it was mainly used, although its successor the AB 41 also saw service in Russia.

63 Carro Armato L.6/40, Italy.

Fiat designed a light tank in 1936 to replace the L.3 series, and after several changes were made, principally to the suspension and the armament, the design emerged as the L.6/40, which was issued to the Italian Army in 1940–1.

The L.6/40 was more or less a scaled-up L.3 with a more powerful engine (a four-cylinder Spa of 70 h.p.) and torsion-bar suspension and equipped with a turret.

With armour to a maximum of 30 mm. and armed with a 20-mm. gun and coaxial 8-mm. machine-gun, the L.6/40 was a considerable improvement on its predecessor. However, with a crew of only two men and still too lightly armed, the tank was not a great success in combat. It was used in action in North Africa from about 1941 onwards and, later, in Russia as a reconnaissance vehicle.

The illustrations both show L.6/40s in European colour schemes; one in the plain greenish-grey used in 1940–1 and the other in a camouflage pattern believed to have been used earlier in the War.

64 Carro Armato M.13/40, Italy.

Retaining the main mechanical features of the M.11/39, the Carro Armato M.13/40 was a great improvement as a fighting vehicle in that the main gun was both much more powerful and was mounted in a fully rotating turret.

The prototype of this 13-ton medium tank appeared early in 1940 and, because of the likelihood of Italy soon entering the War, production was hurried on so that the first production vehicles were ready by July of the same year.

A factor which must have greatly simplified the production of the M.13/40 was that the lower hull was almost identical to that of the M.11/39, although the Spa 8T diesel engine was improved to give 125 h.p. The opportunity was taken at the same time of redesigning some features of the steering and final drive system to make for a more compact and efficient layout. Also, in order to carry the greater weight of the M.13/40, the suspension was strengthened and an extra leaf was added to the semi-elliptic springs.

The main armament consisted of an Ansaldo-built 47-mm. gun, 32 calibres long, mounted coaxially with an 8-mm. Breda model 38 machine-gun in a hydraulically traversed turret. In addition to this, two Breda 38 machine-guns were in a twin mounting in the front right-hand side of the hull, where they had a total traverse of 30 degrees. Armour protection of the M.13/40 was on a 40-mm. basis for the turret front and 30-mm. for the hull.

During the course of production of M.13/40, about mid-1941, a more powerful eight-cylinder Spa engine, the model 15 T of 145 h.p., was introduced and this increased the maximum speed from about 20 m.p.h. to 22 m.p.h. Tanks equipped with this engine and incorporating various other improvements were designated M.14/41. The distinction, however, does not seem to have been very clear-cut and some vehicles completed in 1942 still had the earlier Spa 8T engines. At the same time, it appears that tanks built earlier, when reworked, were sometimes fitted with the Spa 15 T.

First used in action in December 1940 in North Africa, the M.13/40 and its developments were the best Italian tanks to go into service in quantity in the Second World War. Although inferior to contemporary German tanks it was at least comparable in many respects to British cruiser tanks of its era and was one of the very few types of captured tank to be used in some numbers by the British forces—both Australian and United Kingdom armoured regiments used them in Libya in 1941.

The illustrations show the 5th tank, 1st platoon, in the 1st company of an Italian tank battalion in North Africa, about 1941.

65 Tank, Infantry, Mark III, Valentine, U.K.

One of the most reliable of British tanks, the Valentine was designed as a private venture by Vickers-Armstrongs Ltd. and gained its name from the fact that the proposal for this new infantry tank had been deposited with the War Office just before St. Valentine's Day, 1938.

The Valentine was based on the A.9 and A.10 tanks designed by Sir John Carden, who was killed in an aeroplane accident in December 1935. The 30-mm. armour of A.10 was by 1937 no longer considered adequate for an infantry support tank and was rejected for this role, although subsequently the A.10 did enjoy limited production as a heavy cruiser tank. The Valentine, therefore, started with a 65-mm. armour basis (slightly greater than that of Infantry Tank Mark I) but took other features from the A.9 and A.10, including a similar A.E.C. six-cylinder petrol engine and transmission and the same form of suspension. Both hull and turret were more compact, though, and this limited the crew to three men only.

The proposal for the Valentine was at first put aside by the War Office, but in July 1939 a first contract for 275 tanks was placed with Vickers-Armstrongs. Almost at the same time, a further 125 were ordered from the Metropolitan-Cammell Carriage & Wagon Co. Ltd. and 200 from the Birmingham Railway Carriage & Wagon Co. Ltd.

May 1940 was stipulated as the delivery date for the first Vickers-built Valentine and this target was achieved. When the first production vehicle was tested by the War Office (no pilot vehicle had been built—the order being 'off the drawing board') it was found to be generally satisfactory, although the engine cooling needed some im-provements and the tracks were unreliable. It was discovered that although many components appeared to be the same as those on the A.9 and A.10, they were not in fact interchangeable. Steps were taken to correct the faults in the tracks and cooling but the war situation in May–June 1940 made it necessary to obtain new tanks urgently, and a further 600 Valentines were ordered at this time in addition to the 1,325 already by then on order. Canada had been asked in the Spring of 1940 also to participate in Valentine production and had been given a preliminary order for 300.

Output of Valentines rose steadily, while Vickers' engineers corrected their relatively simple faults, so that by mid-1941 they were being delivered at the rate of forty-five per month. They were issued in lieu of Cruiser tanks to equip some of the new armoured divisions, following Britain's build-up of armoured forces after the Dunkirk evacuation, as well as to the Army Tank Brigades—formations which were specifically intended for infantry support.

The Valentine was eventually developed through eleven different Marks, although the main types in use in 1940–1 were the Valentine I, the original model, and Valentine II (Tank, Infantry, Mark III*), in which the petrol engine was replaced by an A.E.C. six-cylinder diesel. The desire for a three-man turret was then met with in the Valentine III. All the earlier Valentines had armament of a 2-pr gun and coaxial 7·92-mm. Besa machine-gun.

Home Defence was necessarily the main role of the Valentine in 1940–1, but some were sent out to North

Africa at the end of 1941. The 8th Royal Tank Regiment was equipped with Valentines at this time and a Valentine II of this unit in desert colours is shown in one of the illustrations. Another Valentine II is shown in the other view, as it appears with the 1st Royal Gloucestershire Hussars (6th Armoured Division) on a United Kingdom training exercise in October 1941.

66 Cars, 4 × 2, Light Reconnaissance, Standard, Marks I and II (Beaverette I and II), U.K.

Most numerous of the many varieties of improvised armoured vehicles built for the defence of the United Kingdom in the emergency after the withdrawal of the British Expeditionary Force from France, the Beaverette was produced in the first instance principally for the defence of aircraft factories. The name was derived from that of Lord Beaverbrook, then Minister of Aircraft Production.

The large quantities of armour plate required could not be spared for these cars and so protection was made up from $\frac{3}{8}$-in. or $\frac{7}{16}$-in. mild-steel plates, with 3-in. oak planks for backing at the front of the vehicle. There was no armour at the rear and no roof. The chassis used was that of the 14-h.p. (R.A.C. rating) passenger car produced by the Standard Motor Company Ltd., of Coventry. This had an engine developing 45 h.p., with a four-speed gearbox. The Beaverette weighed about 2 tons and the maximum speed was 40 m.p.h.

A Beaverette II soon followed the Mark I and this had protection at the rear added. From the front the Mark II could be distinguished by its horizontal (instead of vertical) radiator grilles.

The armament normally consisted of a 0·303-in. Bren light machine-gun firing through a slit in the front plate. This could easily be dismounted for ground action.

Beaverettes I and II were issued during 1940 for aircraft factory defence (as originally planned), to armoured regiments waiting to be re-equipped with tanks, to the Home Guard and to the Royal Air Force for airfield protection. Then, when the Reconnaissance Corps was formed in January 1941 to carry out reconnaissance for infantry divisions, Beaverettes were issued to many battalions of this Corps for home defence and training.

The illustrations show a Beaverette I of the 53rd Battalion The Reconnaissance Corps of the 53rd (Welsh) Division as it appeared in June 1941 and a rear view of a Beaverette II of the 4th/7th Royal Dragoon Guards in July 1940. This unit had been the divisional cavalry regiment of the 2nd Infantry Division in France, where it had lost its light tanks and carriers.

67 Car, 4 × 2, Light Reconnaissance, Humber Mark I (Ironside I) and Car, 4-seater, Armoured Saloon, Humber (Special Ironside), U.K.

In the emergency after the Dunkirk evacuation, the Rootes Group as well as the Standard Motor Company was asked to produce a light armoured car. A prototype, known as Humberette, based on the Humber Super Snipe car chassis, was built during June 1940. This vehicle, with some slight modifications, including W.D. pattern rims for Runflat tyres, was put into production in the following month. Two hundred were built and known as Ironside I. Weighing about $2\frac{3}{4}$ tons, armoured to a maximum of 12 mm. and powered by the Humber 75/80-h.p. six-cylinder engine, these light armoured cars had a top speed of 45 m.p.h. Open-topped vehicles, they carried no fixed armament but were usually equipped with a 0·303-in. Bren light machine-gun or a 0·55-in. Boys anti-tank rifle, as available.

Ironsides were supplied to armoured regiments in lieu of tanks and subsequently to equip armoured car regiments or the Reconnaissance Corps. They were eventually classified as Cars, 4 × 2, Light Reconnaissance.

Another aspect of the defence of the United Kingdom was the need to provide safe transport for Cabinet ministers and members of the Royal Family in the event of air attack or parachute troops landing. The Ironside was selected as the most suitable type of armoured vehicle for adaptation for this purpose, after an old Lanchester armoured car had been tried out and found unsuitable. The detachment of the 12th Royal Lancers responsible for providing the escorts for the Royal Family and Cabinet Ministers received the first Humber Special Ironside armoured saloon on 13 September, 1940, followed by a second five days later, and soon afterwards both the King and Queen and the Prime Minister had travelled in these vehicles.

Although a reasonable degree of comfort was provided in the armoured saloons, they had no windows and so in the later cars built (two of which were received by the 12th Royal

Lancers detachment in December) small bullet-proof windows were provided. At the same time it was no longer felt necessary to provide picks and shovels on the newer armoured saloons, since they were invariably escorted by one or two Guy Armoured Cars, which did carry such equipment.

By January 1941 the invasion emergency had lessened somewhat and in this month the first of two Humber Pullman Protected saloon cars was received. This was a conventional car in appearance but offered some protection against shell splinters or small arms fire. Being much more comfortable than the Special Ironsides, the Protected Pullmans came to be used more and more in their place, although two Ironsides were held on the strength of the escort detachment at least until the end of 1941.

The illustrations show an Ironside I and a Special Ironside of the earlier type without bullet-proof windows.

68 Armoured Car, Dodge, and Lorry, 30 cwt, 4 × 2, Armoured Anti-tank, Bedford, U.K.

Two of the more effective of the many and varied improvised armoured vehicles built in the United Kingdom for home defence in the national emergency in 1940 were these armoured vehicles on Dodge and Bedford lorry chassis respectively.

The Dodge armoured vehicle was conceived by Sir Malcolm Campbell, the racing driver and in 1940 holder of the world water-speed record, and former holder of the world land-speed record. Campbell was then Officer Commanding the Provost Company

of 56th (London) Division. It was ar-
ranged that Leo Villa, Campbell's
Chief Racing Mechanic, should con-
struct a prototype at his (Campbell's)
private workshop in Surrey. This prototype was built on a Fordson lorry
chassis, using $\frac{1}{8}$-in. mild steel. This prototype was then handed over to Briggs
Motor Bodies Ltd., of Dagenham, to
produce a pilot production model in
$\frac{7}{8}$-in. or 1-in. armour plate, using the
same chassis. With some further modifications, including those necessary to
adapt the design to the Dodge chassis
to be used for the production order,
Briggs then went ahead and built
seventy of these armoured cars, the
majority being completed by the end
of August 1940.

Within the limits of what could be
done in the time and with the materials
available, the Dodge Armoured Car
was a well-thought-out design, with
attention paid to the arrangement of
the armour for the best protection and
accessibility of components. The fully-
enclosed hull had several ports for the
operation of crew weapons such as the
0·303-in. Bren machine-gun or the
0·55-in. Boys anti-tank rifle. One
armoured regiment equipped with
these cars mounted the machine-guns
from a shot-down German He.111
bomber in three of them. Later (in
1942) a Home Guard battalion in
Hampshire redesigned the Dodge
armoured car to take a 6-pr (First
World War tank pattern) gun on an
all-round mounting.

These vehicles were known as
Armoured Cars, Dodge, in 1940 and
unofficially as 'Malcolm Campbell'
Armoured Cars. Subsequently they
were classified as 'Cars, four-wheeled,

Light Reconnaissance', although at
around 8 tons they were anything but
light.

The Lorry, 30 cwt, 4 × 2, Armoured
Anti-tank, Bedford, was, by contrast
with the Dodge Armoured Car, a very
simple improvisation on a lorry
chassis. The chassis was the Bedford
model OXA with a 72-h.p. six-cylinder
engine, which was widely used by the
British Army as a load carrier. This
modification consisted of the provision
of an armoured cab for the driver,
behind which was mounted on the
lorry platform a rectangular armoured
box which constituted the fighting
compartment. The only other armour
was plates over the radiator and over
the petrol tanks at the side.
No weapons were permanently
mounted but ports were provided on
all sides for the operation of crew
weapons and it was intended that the
principal armament should be the
0·55-in. Boys anti-tank rifle, a single-
shot weapon suitable for use against
light armoured vehicles. A 0·303-in.
Bren gun was often carried in addition
to, or instead of, the anti-tank rifle.

The illustrations show a Dodge
Armoured Car in the colours of one
of the infantry battalions of the 47th
(London) Division, one of the formations which defended southern England, and a Bedford Armoured Lorry
belonging in 1941 to the 59th Battalion
The Reconnaissance Corps, of the 59th
Infantry Division.

69 Panzerkampfwagen II (Schwimm.), Germany.

A Panzer Battalion was equipped
with a special amphibious version of

PzKpfw II for 'Operation Sea Lion'—
the projected invasion of England in
1940.

The amphibious equipment consisted of a large pontoon built in three
parts which surrounded the tank's hull
at track-guard level and projected at
front and rear. It was attached to the
hull at the return rollers. Propulsion
in water was by means of a propeller
driven by the tank's main engine
through an extension shaft and universal joint. Steering was achieved
by a rudder behind the propeller.
The engine, as well as the hull, was
water-proofed and the turret ring was
sealed by an inflatable rubber tube.
The Schwimmpanzer II was said
to be capable of a speed of up to
6 m.p.h. in smooth water and to be
able to stand up well to seas of Force
4.

Fifty-two sets of equipment were
made by Alkett (Berlin-Spandau),
Bachmann (Ribnitz) and Sachsenberg
(Roslau) and the battalion—Abteilung
A of Panzer Regiment 2—was equipped
by the end of August 1940. Experiments and trials were carried out at the
special amphibious establishment at
Putlos, near Kiel, and a full-scale
rehearsal of the amphibious tanks for
invasion (which included also submersible Panzer IIIs and IVs) was
mounted near Antwerp at the beginning of September.

'Operation Sea Lion' was eventually
cancelled and the Schwimmpanzer IIs
do not seem to have been used after
this, although the submersible PzKpfw
IIIs and IVs were transferred to the
Russian Front for the opening of the
assault across the River Bug in June
1941.

70 **Panzerkampfwagen II
(Flamm.)**, Germany.

After the design of the basic Pzkpfw II
had been stabilised and production was
in progress it was decided to produce
also a faster version ('Schnellkampf-
wagen'), considered more suitable for
issue to light mechanised cavalry
divisions.

Daimler-Benz were asked to draw
up a design for this model in which the
upper hull and turret of the standard
type was to be retained but in which a
revised form of suspension was required
in order to give the higher speeds
needed. The design was undertaken
in 1938 and by the following year 250
tanks were produced. The suspension
used by Daimler-Benz consisted of
four large road wheels each side—of
Christie appearance, but with torsion-
bar springing. This redesign succeeded
in raising the top speed of the tank by
some 5 m.p.h. although the cross-
country performance proved to be
inferior. The new model appeared in
two forms, PzKpfw II, Ausf. D and E,
between which the chief external
difference lay in the design of the front
sprocket.

The need for this fast version of the
Panzer II was not sustained, however,
and in 1940 it was decided to convert
some of these tanks (about 100) into
flamethrower vehicles. (The balance of
PzKpfw II Ds and Es were subsequently converted to S.P. guns.) The
conversion into flamethrowers was
carried out by Wegmann of Kassell.
There were minor variations in the
work done, but essentially it consisted
of the addition of two flame projectors
—one on each front track guard—and

the substitution of a smaller turret (mounting one machine-gun) for the standard turret. The flame fuel carried was sufficient for eighty bursts of 2–3 seconds from the pump-operated projectors. The range was only about 40 yards. The crew consisted of two men.

71 Tank, Heavy, T.O.G. I, U.K.

This interesting tank started life as an alternative to the A.20 (which evolved into the Churchill) as a means of breaching the German Siegfried Line defences. It was felt that the experience of the tank designers of the First World War should be drawn upon, and Sir Albert Stern, who was prominent in tank production in 1917–18, was asked to get together some of his old associates to design an assault tank. A committee was formed under Sir Albert Stern and included Sir Eustace Tennyson d'Eyncourt, Mr. H. Ricardo and General Sir Ernest Swinton and became known as 'The Old Gang', subsequently giving its initials 'TOG' to the new tank evolved in conjunction with the design staff of William Foster & Co. Ltd., who also had played a leading part in the First World War tank design and production.

The tank required was to be able to traverse shelled and waterlogged ground, to be protected against 47-mm. armour-piercing and 105-mm. high-explosive shells at 100 yards and to carry a field gun (capable of piercing 7 ft of reinforced concrete), together with armour-piercing weapons and machine-guns.

Design commenced in February 1940 and T.O.G. I was running in October, by which time its original purpose,

now that France was defeated, no longer existed. However, development was allowed to continue, if only for the sake of research into several interesting features which had been included in the design. These included a Paxman Ricardo Diesel engine of 600 h.p. (the most powerful tank engine in existence in the United Kingdom at the time) and an electric transmission and steering system. (This was later replaced by a hydraulic transmission.)

T.O.G. I as completed broadly resembled the French Char B.1 bis, which had influenced some features of its design. A 75-mm. gun was mounted in the front hull, and a Matilda turret was mounted on the hull roof. However, neither the turret armament nor the side sponsons allowed for in the design appear ever to have been fitted.

The tracks of T.O.G. I were unsprung and with a weight of about 70 tons, not surprisingly, the maximum speed was only $8\frac{1}{2}$ m.p.h., although the trench crossing ability was exceptionally good and comparable to that of the Tank Mark V** of 1918. Steering was difficult because of the exceptionally high ratio of track length on ground to width between track centres.

Development of the T.O.G. series (a second tank, T.O.G. II, was built in 1941) continued sporadically into 1942, and after that they were stored. They were never used in combat.

72 Armoured Command Vehicle, Guy 'Lizard', U.K.

An armoured command vehicle, equipped with wireless, for the use of formation headquarters staff was experimented with by the 1st Tank Brigade about 1937. This was based on a Morris 15-cwt 4 × 2 chassis and proved to be too small for the purpose. Accordingly, following further experiment, a larger vehicle was built on the Guy Lizard 4 × 4 chassis. Armoured command vehicles of this type were issued to formation headquarters in the United Kingdom and in Libya towards the end of 1940 and in early 1941.

Powered by a Gardner five-cylinder engine, the Guy Lizard was unusual for a wheeled armoured vehicle in the British Army in 1940 in using a diesel engine, although the A.E.C. (Matador) Armoured Command Vehicle which succeeded the Lizard in 1941 also had a diesel.

Headquarters, 7th Armoured Division, was using Guy Lizard A.C.V.s in the Spring of 1941, and one is shown here in the Desert camouflage in use at that time. The smaller picture shows the tent extension, normally carried rolled on the side of the vehicle, in use.

73 Armoured Carrier, Wheeled, I.P. Mark I, India.

When it was decided that India's participation in the British Commonwealth war effort should include the manufacture of armoured vehicles, this relatively simple wheeled carrier was chosen as the first type to be produced.

Based on a 113½-in. wheelbase front-engined Ford chassis, with Marmon-Herrington conversion to four-wheel drive, an armoured body of riveted construction was manufactured by the Tata Iron and Steel Works. Only ten of these vehicles were produced between early 1940 and about mid 1941 but after that production, which soon turned to a more advanced rear-engined model of armoured carrier, increased rapidly, with other manufacturers joining Tata.

The Wheeled Carrier, India Pattern, Mark I, was intended to fulfil roughly the same functions as the British tracked carrier series, such as the transport of infantry Bren-gun crews, scouting, etc. As far as is known, Carriers of this first Mark were used only for defence and training in the Indian sub-continent.

74 Tank, Cruiser, Mark V, Covenanter, U.K.

A revised specification for the A.13 led, in 1939, to the London Midland and Scottish Railway being asked to abandon work on an earlier cruiser tank, which was proving unsuccessful, and take on the A.13 instead.

The A.13 Mark III, as it became known, was basically the same specification as the Cruiser Mark IVA with the 30-mm. armour basis, but it was desired to increase the effectiveness of the protection by improved ballistic shape of the armour and by lowering the height of the tank. The suspension was to be the same as the earlier Christie Cruisers, but a new tank engine, specially designed by Meadows, was to be used.

Many difficulties developed in the design of the A.13 Mark III, which came to be known as Cruiser Mark V, to which the name Covenanter was added. These were chiefly centred on the engine, which was the only major untried feature. The cooling was the main problem and the earliest production vehicles which were running by 1940 soon had their engine air intake louvres (situated at the front left-hand side, next to the driver) modified in Army workshops, the resulting vehicles being known as Covenanter IIs. Two further basic Marks, Covenanter III and IV, appeared before the end of 1941 but the cooling problem was never solved really satisfactorily and the Covenanter was declared unfit for overseas service. This tank, nevertheless, played an important part in the defence of the United Kingdom, first in helping to re-equip the 1st Armoured Division, back from France, and later in contributing to the new armoured divisions being raised. The 9th Armoured Division's tanks were almost exclusively Covenanters by the end of 1941. In all, 1,771 Covenanters were built.

The illustrations both show a Covenanter of the 1st Fife and Forfar Yeomanry, one of the armoured regiments of the 28th Armoured Brigade, 9th Armoured Division, in 1941. This tank has the earlier type of axle-shaped external gun mantlet.

75 T-40 (Light Tank), U.S.S.R.

A light amphibious tank, intended to replace earlier models which had been in production during the 1930s, the T-40 first came into service in the early part of 1941. With a two-man crew the T-40 weighed around 6 tons and was armed with a 12·7-mm. heavy machine-gun and a 7·62-mm. machine-gun mounted in the turret, which was offset to the left-hand side of the hull. A 20-mm. cannon was sometimes mounted instead of the heavy machine-gun. Intended to utilise standard automotive parts as far as possible, the T-40 was powered by a GAZ six-cylinder lorry engine of 85 h.p.: this was located at the right-hand side of the hull behind the driver and drove front track sprockets. Independent torsion bars were used for the suspension.

For propulsion in water, a single four-bladed propeller was provided at the rear, the hull nose plate was inclined forwards and flotation tanks were built in. Even so, the armour weight had to be kept down and was to a maximum of 14 mm. only. This disadvantage, coupled with the light armament, led to the T-40's withdrawal from production in 1942.

The illustrations show the slightly modified model T-40A which differed from the T-40 chiefly in having a folding trim-vane (for use in water) just above the top of the nose plate.

76 Armoured Car Mark IV (Ford), Irish Free State.

The outbreak of the Second World War added a greater degree of urgency to the somewhat leisurely experiments that had been carried out in the Irish Free State (as it then was) with the object of re-equipping the Irish Army with armoured cars. With the fall of France, the strong possibility that a German invasion of the United Kingdom would take place and be accompanied or followed up by a violation of Ireland's neutrality, made it a matter of immediate necessity to produce armoured cars. Apart from practical considerations of cost, armoured cars were considered to be more suitable than tanks for employment in the Irish terrain.

The first experimental vehicle (later known as Mark I) was built on an old Morris chassis. This was unsatisfactory and a Ford lorry chassis was used for the next design (Mark II), of which seven were built at the Great Southern Railway Workshops at Inchicore. The Mark II was built on a standard lorry chassis, with the rear of the armoured body extending over the load platform, but it was felt that a shorter wheelbase was desirable.

When it was established that the Ford chassis could satisfactorily be shortened, arrangements by Messrs. Thompson's of Carlow went ahead to produce the prototype of the Mark III car. This vehicle, which was completed on 9 August 1940, had an armoured hull made up from $\frac{1}{2}$-in. mild-steel plates, as armour plate was not available in Ireland. It was found to offer satisfactory protection against small arms fire, however, and all subsequent cars were made from mild steel. The turret of the Mark III prototype was of armour plate and mounted a Hotchkiss machine-gun. Turrets of obsolete Peerless twin-turret armoured cars which had been taken out of service were available and were used for all fourteen Mark IIIs, including the prototype, which were built.

The general war situation at the end of 1940 led the Irish Department of Defence to decide to have made a further twenty-one armoured cars similar to the Mark IIIs. A new turret and mounting for a Vickers 0·303-in. water-cooled machine-gun was de-signed for the new cars. The first of these, which were designated Mark IV, were completed early in March 1941.

After various modifications, the Irish-built armoured cars turned out to be quite suitable for employment in Ireland, but some Mark IVs were even used in the Congo with the Irish contingent of the United Nations Force—twenty-five years after they were constructed.

77 Cockatrice and Heavy Cockatrice Flamethrowers, U.K.

The Cockatrice type of mobile flame-thrower was developed during 1941 by Lagonda Ltd. as a vehicle for the defence of airfields or harbours. They were based on a prototype flame-thrower vehicle, using an armoured Commer lorry chassis, built by Lagonda's in the Autumn of 1940.

The Cockatrice's flame projector was mounted in a small turret on the roof of the vehicle: it used 8 gallons of fuel per second and had a range of 100 yards. Two forms of chassis were used, both lightly armoured—the 4×4 Bedford model QL and the 6×6 A.E.C. (of the type used by the R.A.F. as refuelling tenders and crane lorries). The arrangement was, however, the same for both models, the main difference being that a greater supply of fuel for the flamethrower could be carried in the heavier A.E.C. vehicle. Both types carried as supplementary armament two light machine-guns on an open anti-aircraft mounting, at the rear of the vehicle.

Sixty Bedford Cockatrices were constructed for the defence of Royal

Naval airfields and six of the A.E.C. heavy Cockatrices were built for the Royal Air Force.

78 Tank, Infantry, Mark IV, Churchill, U.K.

A General Staff Specification, A.20, for a heavy infantry tank capable of breaching the defences of the German Siegfried Line, was drawn up in September 1939. This called for 60-mm. frontal protection and a speed of 10 m.p.h. Consideration was given to various forms of armament, ranging in calibre from the 2-pr (40-mm.) anti-tank gun to a low-velocity 3.7-in. (95-mm.) howitzer. Combinations of turrets, hull mountings and sponsons were also considered but the final decision was for a turret (with 2-pr and coaxial Besa machine-gun) like that of the Infantry Mark II, a second 2-pr mounted in the front hull, and a Besa machine-gun in a sponson on each side of the hull.

Harland & Wolff Ltd., the Belfast engineers and shipbuilders, were asked to design and supply four mild steel prototypes of A.20, or Infantry Tank Mark IV. The first of these was running by the middle of 1940 and although the armament had not been fitted its mechanical performance was disappointing, both engine and gearbox turning out to be unsatisfactory.

Vauxhall Motors Ltd., manufacturers of cars and Bedford lorries, were then asked to design a new 350-h.p. engine. This was done successfully, but it was decided to replace the A.20 specification with a revised one, A.22, in which, nevertheless, the new Bedford engine was incorporated. Vauxhall

Motors, assisted by Dr. H. E. Merritt, Director of Tank Design, undertook to design and produce the new version of Infantry Tank Mark IV.

The date was then July 1940, so the utmost urgency was essential so that the greatest possible number of tanks could soon become available for Home Defence. By a remarkable effort the first prototype vehicle was actually being tested by the end of 1940, and the first production batch of fourteen Tanks, Infantry, Mark IV, was completed by Vauxhall Motors in June 1941—only a year from the commencement of design. During this time arrangements were made for mass production to be undertaken by a group of eleven manufacturers, under the overall control of Vauxhall Motors.

In ordering the A.22 'off the drawing board' it was expected that faults would come to light in the production vehicles, and many difficulties did in fact arise. However, the national emergency justified the action taken and it was felt that in the event of invasion even immobile tanks used as blockhouses were better than none at all.

One of the most interesting features of the Infantry Mark IV was the Merritt-Brown four-speed gearbox (five speeds in the very earliest vehicles) through which a controlled differential steering system was provided. The Bedford Twin-Six power unit was made up of two six-cylinder Bedford truck engines—a device which produced the necessary power, and must have simplified the supply of spares, although accessibility for maintenance was not good. A new pattern of suspension for British tanks was used, consisting of small diameter steel road wheels mounted independently on short trailing arms and sprung on vertical coil springs. The hull was made up of armour plates bolted on to a riveted steel box; the turret was a casting.

The original armament consisted of a 2-pr gun and coaxial 7·92-mm. Besa machine-gun in the turret and a 3-in. howitzer, firing high-explosive ammunition, in the hull front, next to the driver. A second model, known at first as Tank, Infantry, Mark IVA, had a second Besa machine-gun in place of the 3-in. howitzer. When, in June 1941, names were adopted officially for British tanks, these two models became known as Churchill I and Churchill II respectively. In all, 5,640 Churchills were produced by the end of the War, of which something like 2,000 were built as Churchill I's or II's.

Development of a 6-pr-armed Churchill began in 1941, but the Churchill I and II were the only types in service before 1942, when they were exclusively employed on Home Defence. The illustrations show a Churchill II of the Polish Army Tank Brigade, which had begun to receive Churchill tanks in the United Kingdom by the end of 1941, and a Churchill I of the 9th Battalion Royal Tank Regiment, which formed part of one of the newly raised British Army Tank Brigades.

79 N.L.E. Trenching Machine, Mark I, U.K.

Unique, and certainly one of the most interesting devices of the Second World War, the N.L.E. Trenching Machine was overtaken by events so that no opportunity ever occurred for its employment in the role for which it was intended.

Originating in the fertile brain of Mr. Winston Churchill (in 1939, as in 1914, First Lord of the Admiralty) as a means of cutting through enemy defence lines, instructions were given in November to the Director of Naval Construction for experiments to be carried out. A machine which could cut a trench across no-man's-land in the space of one night, through which infantry and tanks could follow, was required. Drawings were made and a scale model was built by the Bassett-Lowke model railway firm. This model was demonstrated by Mr. Churchill during December and January to Cabinet ministers and senior British and French Army officers to some effect, for in February 1940 the Cabinet approved the construction of 240 full-size machines, known under the code name of 'White Rabbit No. 6', later changed to 'Cultivator'. The Department of Naval Land Equipment was formed to control the project and overall responsibility for production was given to Ruston-Bucyrus Ltd., Lincoln, a firm with long experience in the manufacture of civilian earth-moving equipment.

There were many difficulties in the production of such a large and unconventional machine (the prototype, when completed, weighed some 130 tons and was 77 ft 6 in. long), not the least of which was the discovery, in April 1940, that the projected Rolls-Royce engines could not be used, since all Rolls-Royce engine production capacity was required for the Royal

Air Force. Then, in May, the German campaign in France so altered the situation that the bulk of the scheme was cancelled. However, work on a limited scale was allowed to proceed on the grounds that there might, in the future, be some special tactical use for the machines or that they might, in an invasion emergency, be useful for the rapid digging of defensive ditches in the United Kingdom.

The first prototype, known officially as N.L.E. Trenching Machine Mark I, was completed by July 1941: it carried the name 'Nellie I' on its side. In overall appearance, the N.L.E. Trenching Machine resembled a lengthened British First World War tank (some of Sir William Tritton's early drawings had, in fact, been referred to for various parts of the design) but without the sponsons and with a large V-shaped plough blade covering the front section, which was hinged. This front section contained a cutting cylinder, equipped with hardened steel blades.

When starting to cut a trench, the cutting cylinder was lowered and cut into the ground as the machine moved forward (at a speed of $\frac{1}{2}$ m.p.h.) and gradually downwards into the depression that had been made. A point was soon reached where the tip of the plough blade entered into the earth ahead of the cutting cylinder and as the machine got deeper the plough took the first cut and eased the work of the cutting blades. The soil removed was ejected either side of the machine by conveyor belts. The maximum depth that could be cut in loam was 5 ft., but the soil deposited on the parapets added about another 3 ft above the surface. An armoured cab was provided

for the driver, but armour was not used elsewhere, since when dug in the machine had provided its own protection.

Nellie I was powered by two Davey-Paxman diesel engines, one to propel the machine and the other to drive the cutters.

In the end, only six N.L.E. Trenching Machines, including the prototype, were completed and were kept in store until after the Siegfried Line was breached in the Summer of 1945 by less unconventional means.

80 **Tank, Light, M.3 (Stuart I),** U.S.A.

Developed from the M2A4 light tank, the M.3 incorporated improvements found to be necessary from experience with the earlier vehicle. The main change, from the mechanical point of view, lay in the introduction of a large trailing idler wheel in place of the idler of the M2A4: this helped to improve stability.

Designed, like its predecessor, at the Rock Island Arsenal, the M.3 coming after the outbreak of war in Europe was able to benefit from what up-to-date information could be obtained about tanks in combat, and the 25.4-mm. maximum protection of the M2A4 was more than doubled to a 51-mm. standard. The armament remained the same as the M2A4's.

The same engine—the 250-h.p. Continental radial—was retained and, in spite of the increased weight, the M.3 had roughly the same performance as the M2A4. In some of the later vehicles to be produced, however, a Guiberson nine-cylinder diesel engine was used, because of a shortage of Continental engines.

The Light Tank M.3 entered into production in March 1941 and some of the earliest vehicles to be completed were in the hands of British tank units in the Middle East by August of the same year, where they were a valuable addition to British strength in the desert battles.

The M.3 was named Stuart I by the War Office, who classified it this time as a light cruiser tank by virtue of its armament and armour. The two sponson machine-guns were, however, removed in most cases in tanks used in action. A weak point about the M.3, particularly in the open desert fighting, was its lack of range, and this was later rectified by the addition of jettisonable supplementary fuel tanks.

The illustrations both show tanks in British use in North Africa in 1941. Tank 'Crossbow' is a Stuart I of 'C' Squadron, 8th King's Royal Irish Hussars, one of the first regiments to receive this type.

APPENDIX

Armoured Fighting Vehicle Camouflage and Markings 1939-41

In the coloured illustrations, considerable effort has been made to show camouflage colours as accurately as possible and tactical and other markings for specific vehicles have been included wherever practicable. However, in some cases, information has been unobtainable or, at best, sketchy. Apart from the difficulties of colour reproduction in a book, the colours used on the actual armoured fighting vehicles often varied for many reasons—the exact colours for camouflage were not always considered important and wide discretion was allowed to unit or tank commanders; the quality control on paints issued—always difficult to maintain—sometimes allowed quite wide variations; and colours, once applied, could sometimes be changed out of all recognition by ageing, frequently helped by terrain such as desert sand.

For those wishing to go further into this subject, much useful information is published in the journals *Tankette* (Editor, Max Hundleby, 4 Low Croft, Woodplumpton, Preston, PR4 OAU, England) and *AFV News* (Editor, George Bradford, R.R.No.2, Preston, Ontario, Canada).

Belgium

Overall khaki (brown) shade. Vehicle registration number carried at front and rear preceded by a small rectangle in the national colours. A small roundel in three colours was often carried on turret or hull. Sometimes unit signs, such as the wild boar of the Chasseurs Ardennais, were also shown on A.F.V.s.

Czechoslovakia

A three-colour camouflage scheme, applied in irregular blotches. Vehicle registration number carried at front and rear.

Finland

Overall dark green, for winter operations covered in white blotches or sometimes wholly in white. The Finnish swastika in medium blue outlined in white was carried on A.F.V. turrets by 1941.

France

In some cases a single overall colour was used but generally one of several more or less standard schemes, using patches of two or, more usually, three colours. Sometimes the meeting point of different colours was outlined in a dark colour. The vehicle registration number was carried at the front and rear of the hull preceded by a blue/white/red tricolour rectangle. A roundel or rectangle in the national colours was sometimes carried on the turret or hull. Tactical markings, when used, varied widely: sometimes playing card signs to denote sub-units, or large numbers to distinguish individual tanks. Most of the Chars B carried individual tank names.

A medium to dark grey, overall, was generally used throughout the greater part of this period in all European operations and even in some tanks in North Africa. The latter were usually repainted in sand yellow, however. There appear to have been some wide variations in the grey used, ranging from a very light shade to almost black.

In the Polish campaign a white cross on turret and/or hull was used as a national marking. This was retained on some vehicles in 1940 but generally had been replaced by a black cross outlined in white or, sometimes, by only the white outline of the cross painted straight on to the vehicle.

A tactical number was usually carried, originally in white on a small black lozenge-shaped plate (at the sides and/or rear of the vehicles), later to be supplemented by, and eventually replaced by, a large number on the turret or hull. The large number was either in white; in red or black, outlined in white; or simply in white outline. The system for allocating these tactical numbers was usually as follows, although there were exceptions to the general rule.

R 01	regimental commander
R 02	regimental adjutant
R 03	ordnance or signals officer
R 04, etc.	regimental staff
I 01	commander of I battalion
I 02	adjutant of I battalion
I 03	ordnance officer of I battalion
I 04, etc.	staff of I battalion
101	officer commanding 1st company, I battalion
102	2nd-in-command, 1st company, I battalion
111	Leader, 1st platoon, 1st company, I battalion
112	2nd vehicle, 1st platoon, 1st company, I battalion (113 = 3rd vehicle, etc.)
133	3rd vehicle, 3rd platoon, 1st company, I battalion
201	officer commanding 2nd company, I battalion
301	officer commanding 3rd company, I battalion
II01	commander of II battalion, and so on for H.Q. st a
401 501 601	officers commanding 4th, 5th and 6th companies, II battalion

Self-propelled guns often carried on the hull a letter denoting the battery to which the vehicle belonged.

A divisional sign, usually small, was often stencilled on the hull of A.F.Vs, usually on or near the driver's plate. This was in yellow or, more rarely, in white. Some divisions later introduced larger, coloured signs.

Armoured cars (which usually did not carry tactical numbers) and half-tracks, but not tanks, had vehicle registration number plates at front and rear. Wehrmacht vehicles carried the prefix WH and SS vehicles the double flash of lightning symbol. Armoured cars and artillery vehicles also often carried small symbolic signs indicating the type of unit and the sub-unit within that unit.

Holland

Overall shade of olive green. Vehicle registration number plates carried at front and rear. Before mobilisation the numbers were white on dark blue plates. After mobilisation black numbers on orange plates were used.

India

Armoured vehicles built in India intended for service in the Middle East were generally painted in the schemes used in that theatre of war.

Irish Free State

Usually overall light grey. Vehicle registration numbers (of the civilian series for the City and County of Dublin) were normally carried at front and rear, in white.

Italy

A camouflage scheme of dark rust red and dark green was generally superseded by 1940 by an overall dark greenish grey for A.F.V.s in Italy. In North Africa, vehicles were painted a sand yellow.

Tactical markings consisted firstly of the regimental number in white arabic figures and the battalion number in white Roman figures. These were usually carried on rear surfaces of the tank's fighting compartment. Battalion command tanks were denoted on the turret or hull by a rectangle divided vertically into red, blue and yellow strips or, where there were only two companies in the battalion, red and blue only. The company signs, carried on the sides and rear of the turret (or hull, in turretless vehicles) were as follows:

   1st company—red rectangle
   2nd company—blue rectangle
   3rd company—yellow rectangle
   4th company—green rectangle

Platoons were indicated by one, two or three vertical white bars on the company sign, indicating 1st, 2nd or 3rd platoon, respectively. The position of the individual tank in the platoon was shown by an arabic number in white or the company colour above or below the company sign.

From early 1941 the vehicle registration number was added at front and rear. The number was in black on a white plate, preceded by 'RoEto' (Regio Esercito = Royal Army) in red.

Poland

A two-colour scheme in shades of green and brown seems generally to have been used in 1939, although there was also an earlier scheme using three colours, outlined in a darker shade.

South Africa

A.F.V.s in South Africa are believed to have been painted in a sand colour. Registration numbers when carried were prefixed by the letter 'U' (for Union Defence Force). South African-built armoured cars sent to the Middle East were usually painted in the colours used there.

Sweden

A camouflage system of patches in grey, brown, green and black, in winter overpainted in white. The Swedish insignia of three crowns was carried on A.F.V.s at this time although it was later dropped and eventually (after 1941) superseded by a small reproduction of the Swedish flag. The crowns seemingly reversed the colours of the Swedish coat of arms and were apparently blue on a yellow background.

U.S.S.R.

Russian tanks were usually painted in a single colour of a green or brown shade. Sometimes, but only infrequently, a disruptive pattern in a dark shade was added. A.F.V.s in winter were frequently painted or whitewashed white.

Sometimes (but rarely in combat) a red star was shown on the turret or hull. Slogans—generally of a patriotic nature—were more frequently shown on tanks in combat. Call signs, usually painted in white (black on winter-camouflaged A.F.V.s) and enclosed in a geometric shape, came increasingly to be exhibited during the Second World War.

United Kingdom

The colour most frequently used for British A.F.V.s in Europe early in 1939 was an overall shade of dark green known as Middle Bronze Green (British Standards Institution specification No. 381—1930, colour No. 23). A darker version (Deep Bronze Green, colour No. 24) was sometimes used instead.

In mid 1939 instructions were given for A.F.V.s to be camouflaged so that a disruptive pattern of the dark colour (Deep Bronze Green) was added. This was the standard scheme, but where a lighter effect was desired, larger areas were painted in Light Bronze Green (B.S.I. No. 381—1930, colour No. 22), thus leaving the Middle Bronze Green as the darker shade. In special circumstances a third colour (normally a shade of brown) could be added to either disruptive pattern.

Towards the end of 1941, a khaki brown colour, known as Standard Camouflage Colour No. 2 (later published in B.S.I. No. 987c—1942) was authorised as an alternative to Middle Bronze Green but it was laid down that the dark disruptive colour should be Standard Camouflage Colour No. 1A (also later included in

B.S.I. No. 987c)—a very dark brown. However, it appears that various lighter shades of khaki brown (such as Shade No. 4 in B.S.I. No. 987c) were sometimes used as a basic colour both before and after the War Office instruction was issued.

A.F.V.s in the Middle East were at first painted in an overall sand yellow colour but in 1940 a new scheme in radiating bands of colour was introduced. The lightest colour (sand yellow) was at the bottom, a blue-grey next and a dark colour on top. Alternatively, two or three colours were used in an irregular pattern instead of in straight lines. The colours used in these schemes appear to have been based on B.S.I. No. 381–1930, Colours Nos. 28, 34, 61 and 64, among others, and there were variations.

Formation signs were carried by British A.F.V.s, normally at the front and rear of the hull. All British units were allotted a unit code sign, usually applicable to the type of unit, which was unique *only* in conjunction with the formation sign. The code sign was a white number on a coloured square. Code numbers were usually allocated to armoured regiments in the brigade in accordance with their seniority in the Army List.

The most important of these unit code numbers for A.F.V.'s in 1939–41 were as follows:

| | 1939–40 | | 1940–1 | |
	Europe	Middle East	Europe	Middle East
Armoured Division				
Headquarters (I) Armoured Brigade	3	?	50	71
Armoured Regiment (Battalion) (1)	4	24	51	40
Armoured Regiment (Battalion) (2)	5	25	52	85
Armoured Regiment (Battalion) (3)	6	26	53	67
Headquarters (II) Armoured Brigade	7	?	60	71
Armoured Regiment (Battalion) (1)	8	28	61	40
Armoured Regiment (Battalion) (2)	9	29	62	86
Armoured Regiment (Battalion) (3)	10	30	63	67
Armoured Car Regiment	129	14	47	76

(Army Troops)

The coloured square of the unit code sign was red for Headquarters and armoured units of (I) Brigade and green for Headquarters and units of (II) Brigade. Colours for armoured car regiments varied. The units of the (II) Brigade in the Middle East were distinguished by a different Brigade sign in conjunction with the unit code number. 1st Army Tank Brigade with the B.E.F. used the same unit code numbers as for the (I) Brigade of an Armoured Division with a white bar added above the numbers. Later, various numbers were used for Army Tank Brigades.

Tanks of 6th Armoured Division did not carry unit code numbers but had instead coloured patches below the divisional sign.

Tactical signs for A.F.V.s in 1939–40 were at first in the form of coloured pennants painted on the tank and/or flown from the wireless aerial. In 1940 a more or less standardised system using hollow geometric shapes painted on turrets and/or hulls was adopted as follows:

Regimental (Battalion) Headquarters—diamond
'A' Squadron (Company)—triangle
'B' Squadron (Company)—square
'C' Squadron (Company)—circle
'D' Squadron (Company)—vertical bar

These tactical signs were in the following colours:

Senior Regiment in Brigade—red
Second Regiment in Brigade—yellow
Third Regiment in Brigade—blue
Fourth Regiment in Brigade—green

In armoured formations only armoured car regiments (after 1940) or infantry motor battalions had a fourth squadron or company and the fourth unit in an armoured brigade was usually the motor battalion.

British A.F.V.s frequently carried individual names, usually allocated in associated groups for squadrons and/or sub units, often bearing the same initial letter as the Squadron letter. In the Battalions of the Royal Tank Regiment, however, the name in most cases began with the letter equivalent to the Battalion number (e.g. 4th Battalion tank names—Destroyer, Devil, Duck, etc.).

The War Department registration number (prefixed by T for tanks, F for armoured cars and so on) was carried in white on the front and rear of the hull and/or hull or turret sides, according to the type of vehicle. Civilian registration numbers ceased to be allocated to W.D. vehicles early in the War and the plates carrying these were usually no longer displayed after 1940.

Different A.F.V. recognition signs were used at various times. In North Africa from about November 1941 onwards these consisted of vertical white/red/white strips painted on the turrets and/or hulls of tanks. In France in 1940 a white square appears to have served for this function.

Finally, British A.F.V.s nearly always carried a bridge group number, equivalent to the maximum loaded weight of the vehicle. This number was in black on a yellow disc or within a yellow ring.

U.S.A.

An overall shade of green was used, ranging from a fairly light olive colour to a quite dark green in different units and vehicles. U.S.A. vehicle registration numbers were carried on hull sides in white or sometimes pale blue.

Tanks often carried their unit number on their turrets, together with letters and numbers indicating the position of the vehicle in the unit. Vehicles supplied to the United Kingdom were, of course, painted in the British colours appropriate to the theatre of war where they were employed.

The dimensions quoted here should be taken as a rough guide only: in some cases they are approximations
It has not been practicable here to quote gun calibre lengths, but it should be borne in mind that thes
gun in 1939 had a far lower penetrative ability than, for example, the much longer 37-mm. guns used i
In the tables 'm.g.' has been used to denote rifle-calibre machine-guns and 'h.m.g.' for weapons of aroun

Ref. No.	Type	Weight tons	Length ft in.	Width ft in.	Height ft in.	Armour max. m.m.	Armament
	U.K.						
39	Light, Mk. VIB	5·2	12 11½	6 9	7 3½	14	1 h.m.g., 1 m.g.
49	Cruiser, Mk. I	12·0	19 3	8 4	8 4	14	1 2-pr, (40 mm.), 3 m.g.
50	Cruiser, Mk. IIA	13·75	18 1	8 3½	8 6	30	1 2-pr, 2 m.g.
51	Cruiser, Mk. IV	14·75	19 9	8 4	8 6	30	1 2-pr, 1 m.g.
74	Cruiser, Mk. V	18·0	19 0	8 7	7 4	40	1 2-pr, 1 m.g.
40	Infantry, Mk. I	11·0	15 11	7 6	6 1½	60	1 h.m.g., or 1 m.g.
52	Infantry, Mk. II	26·5	18 5	8 6	8 0	78	1 2-pr, 1 m.g.
65	Infantry, Mk. III	16·0	17 9	8 7½	7 5½	65	1 2-pr, 1 m.g.
78	Infantry, Mk. IV	38·5	24 5	10 8	8 2	102	1 2-pr, 1 3-in., 1 m.g.
25	Carrier, Bren	4·0	12 0	6 11	4 6	12	1 m.g.
	Germany						
15	PzKpfw IB	5·7	14 6	6 9	5 7	15	2 m.g.
20	PzKpfw IIc	8·7	15 7	7 0	6 6	30	1 2-cm., 1 m.g.
44	PzKpfw IIIE	19·15	17 7⅞	9 7	8 0	30	1 3·7 cm., 2 m.g.
45	PzKpfw IVB	17·42	19 3	9 4	8 6	30	1 7·5-cm., 1 m.g.
60	Stu. G. III	21·65	18 0	9 8	6 4	50	1 7·5-cm.
	France						
9	AMR 35 ZT	6·0	14 2	6 0	5 10	13	1 25-mm. or 1 h.m.g. or 1 m.g.
8	AMC 35 ACG 1	14·5	15 0	7 4	7 8	40	1 47-mm., 1 m.g.
5	CL R.35	9·8	13 4	6 2	6 8	45	1 37-mm., 1 m.g.
6	CL H.35	11·4	14 1	6 0	7 1	34	1 37-mm., 1 m.g.
16	CL FCM.36	12·8	14 11	7 2	7 4	40	1 37-mm., 1 m.g.
3	CM D.2	20	16 10	7 3	8 10	40	1 47-mm., 2 m.g.
7	CC S.35	20	17 8	7 1	9 0	55	1 47-mm., 1 m.g.
4	CB B.1 bis	32	21 9	8 3	9 4	60	1 75-mm., 1 47-mm., 2 m.g.
11	Chenillette UE	2·0	8 10	5 7	3 5	7	Nil
	Italy						
12	L.3/35	3·2	10 4	4 7	4 2	13·5	2 m.g.
63	L.6/40	6·8	12 5	6 4	6 8	30	1 20-mm., 1 m.g.
41	M.11/39	11·0	15 6	7 2	7 6½	30	1 37-mm., 2 m.g.
64	M.13/40	14·0	16 2	7 3	7 9	40	1 47-mm., 3 m.g.
	U.S.A.						
37	Light M2A4	10·8	14 7	8 4	8 4	25·4	1 37-mm., 4 m.g.
80	Light M.3	12·23	14 10	7 6	8 3	51	1 37-mm., 2-4 m.g.
	Poland						
2	TK3	2·43	8 6	5 10	4 4	8	1 20-mm. or 1 m.g.
17	7TP	11·0	15 1	7 11	7 1	40	1 37-mm., 1 m.g.
	U.S.S.R.						
22	T-26B	9·55	15 0	8 0½	8 4	25	1 45-mm., 1 m.g.
75	T-40A	6·2	14 0	7 8	5 8	14	1 h.m.g., 1 m.g.
32	T-28C	32·0	24 5½	9 2½	9 3	80	1 76·2-mm., 3 m.g.
23	BT-7	13·8	18 8	8 0	7 6	22	1 45-mm., 1 m.g.
61	T-34/76A	26·3	20 0	9 9½	8 0	45	1 76·2-mm., 2 m.g.
33	T-35	45	31 6	10 6	11 3	30	1 76·2-mm., 2 45-mm., 5 m.g.
55	KV IB	47·5	22 3½	10 11½	10 8	110	1 76·2-mm., 3 m.g.
56	KV II	53·0	22 3½	10 11½	12 0	110	1 152-mm., 2 m.g.
	Czechoslovakia						
13	LT-35	10·5	14 10	7 0	7 2½	35	1 37-mm., 2 m.g.
30	LT-38	8·5	14 11	6 7½	7 9	25	1 37-mm., 2 m.g.
	Sweden						
35	Strv. m/39	9·0	15 0	6 6½	6 4	24	1 37-mm., 2 m.g.

erformance figures are also approximate—they can vary widely under different conditions.
e a major factor in performance. Short-barrelled weapons like the French 37-mm. widely used as a tank
e U.S. M2A4 and M3 Light Tanks.
2–15 mm., but below 20 mm.

RMOURED VEHICLES

Engine	H.P.	Speed m.p.h.	Range miles	Crew	Notes
Meadows	88	35	130	3	
A.E.C.	150	25	100	6	
A.E.C.	150	16	100	5	
Nuffield Liberty	340	30	90	4	
Meadows	300	31	100	4	
Ford	70	8	80	2	
A.E.C. (diesel)	174	15	70	4	
A.E.C.	135	15	90	3	Valentine II had diesel engine
Bedford	350	15·5	90	5	Churchill II had second m.g. instead of 3-in. how.
Ford	65/85	30	160	3	U.S. or Canadian engines—85 h.p.
Maybach	100	25	90	2	
Maybach	140	25	90	3	
Maybach	300	25	137	5	
Maybach	300	25	124	5	
Maybach	300	25	101	4	
Renault	80	37	125	2	
Renault	180	25	100	3	
Renault	82	12·5	87	2	
Hotchkiss	75	17·5	81	2	
Berliet (diesel)	91	15	200	2	
Renault	150	15	96	3	
Somua	190	25	160	3	
Renault	300	17·5	87	4	
Renault	35	18	60	2	
Spa (Fiat)	43	26	75	2	
Spa	70	26	125	2	
Spa (diesel)	105	20	125	3	
Spa (diesel)	125	20	125	4	
Continental	250	37	70	4	
Continental	250	36	60	4	
Ford	40	28	125	2	
Saurer (diesel)	110	20	100	3	
GAZ(Armstrong-Siddeley)	90	17·5	140	3	
GAZ	85	26	210	2	
M-17L	500	20	110	6	
M-17T	450	45/33	310	3	Speed 45 m.p.h. on wheels, 33 m.p.h. on tracks
V-234 (diesel)	500	31	188	4	
M-17M	500	18	94	10	
V-2K (diesel)	550	22	156	5	
V-2K (diesel)	550	16	100	6	
Skoda	120	25	120	4	
Praga	125	35	125	4	
Scania Vabis	142	28	150	3	

Ref. No.	Type	Weight tons	Length ft in.		Width ft in.		Height ft in.		Armour max. m.m.	Armament
	U.K. and South Africa									
27	Morris CS9/LAC	4·2	15	7½	6	8½	7	3	7	1 anti-tank rifle, 1 m.g.
53	Guy I	5·2	13	6	6	9	7	6	15	1 h.m.g., 1 m.g.
54	Car, Scout, Mk I	2·8	10	5	5	7½	4	11	30	1 m.g.
67	Ironside I	2·8	14	4	6	2	6	10	12	1 anti-tank rifle *or* 1 m.g.
57	S.A. Reconn. Car, Mk. II	6·0	16	0	6	6	7	11	12	2 m.g.
	Germany									
19	SdKfz 231 (6-rad.)	5·9	18	4	6	0	7	4	14·5	1 2-cm., 1 m.g.
28	SdKfz 231 (8-rad.)	8·15	19	1	7	3	7	10	14·5	1 2-cm., 1 m.g.
58	SdKfz 222	4·7	15	6	6	7	6	9	14·5	1 2-cm., 1 m.g.
42	SdKfz 251	8·37	19	0	6	11	5	9	12	1 m.g.
59	SdKfz 250	5·61	15	0	6	5	5	6	12	1 m.g.
	France									
10	AMD Panhard 178	8·07	15	9	6	7	7	7	20	1 25-mm., 1 m.g.
	Italy									
62	AB 40	6·48	16	5	6	4	7	8	18	3 m.g.
	U.S.A.									
38	Scout Car, M3A1	5·03	18	3	6	5½	6	1	12	1 h.m.g., 1–2 m.g.
	Poland									
1	wz 34	2·2	11	10½	6	3	7	3	6	1 37-mm. *or* 1 m.g.
	U.S.S.R.									
21	BA-32	7·5	16	2	6	3	8	0	15	1 45-mm., 2 m.g.
	Sweden									
34	Pb. m/39.40	7·8	16	9	7	6½	7	3	18	1 20-mm., 3 m.g.
	Holland									
48	D.A.F.	6·0	15	2	6	7½	6	7	12	1 37 mm., 3 m.g.

Engine	H.P.	Speed m.p.h.	Range miles	Crew	Wheel arrangement	Notes
Morris Commercial	96·2	45	240	4	4 × 2	
Meadows	53	40	210	3	4 × 4	
Daimler	55	55	200	2	4 × 4	
Humber	80	45	—	3	4 × 2	
Ford	95	50	200	4	4 × 4	
(See text)	65–70	37	150	4	6 × 4	
Büssing NAG	155	53	186	4	8 × 8	
Horch	81	46	175	3	4 × 4	
Maybach	100	31	186	12	½-T	
Maybach	100	37	198	6	½-T	
Panhard	105	45	187	4	4 × 4	
Spa	80	46	250	4	4 × 4	
Hercules	110	55	250	8	4 × 4	
Citroen	20	22	156	2	4 × 2	
GAZ (Ford)	85	34	155	4	6 × 4	
Volvo	135	44	—	6	4 × 4	
Ford	95	37	181	6	6 × 4	

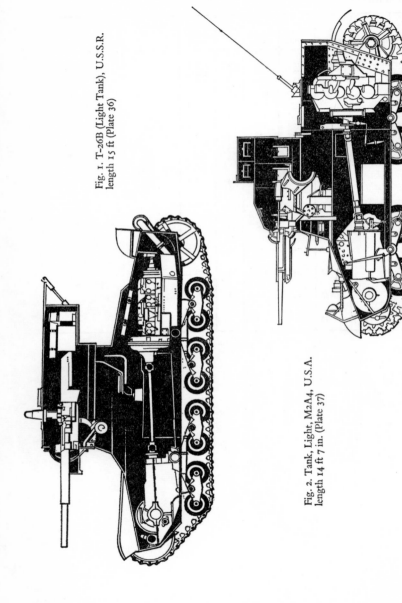

Fig. 1. T-26B (Light Tank), U.S.S.R.
length 15 ft (Plate 36)

Fig. 2. Tank, Light, M2A4, U.S.A.
length 14 ft 7 in. (Plate 37)

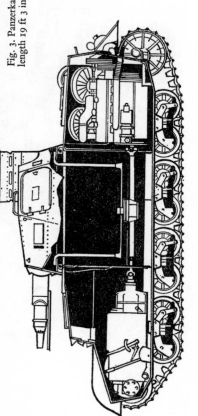

Fig. 3. Panzerkampfwagen IV, Ausf. A, Germany
length 19 ft 3 in. (Plate 45)

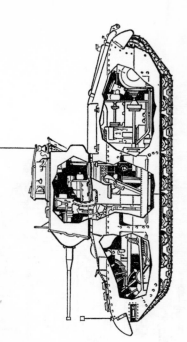

Fig. 4. Tank, Infantry, Mark II, Matilda, U.K.
length 18 ft 5 in. (Plate 52)

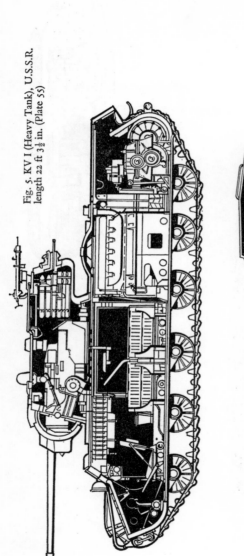

Fig. 5. KV I (Heavy Tank), U.S.S.R.
length 22 ft 3½ in. (Plate 55)

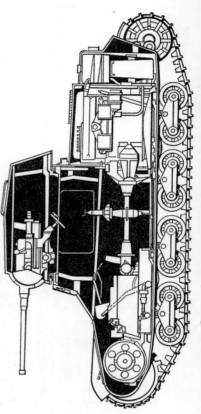

Fig. 6. Carro Armato M.13/40, Italy
length 16 ft 2 in. (Plate 64)

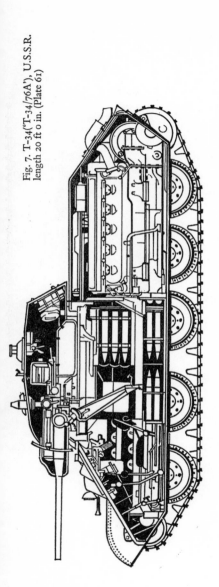

Fig. 7. T-34('T-34/76A'), U.S.S.R.
length 20 ft 0 in. (Plate 61)

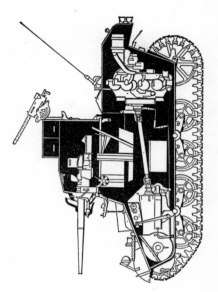

Fig. 8. Tank, Light, M3 (Stuart I), U.S.A.
length 14 ft 10 in. (Plate 80)